# ENERGY-EFFICIENT OPERATION OF COMMERCIAL BUILDINGS

*Redefining the
Energy Manager's Job*

## Peter Herzog

**McGraw-Hill**
New York San Francisco Washington, D.C. Auckland Bogotá
Caracas Lisbon London Madrid Mexico City Milan
Montreal New Delhi San Juan Singapore
Sydney Tokyo Toronto

*McGraw-Hill*

*A Division of The McGraw·Hill Companies*

1 2 3 4 5 6 7 8 9 0 DOC/DOC 9 0 1 0 9 8 7 6

ISBN 0–07–028468–7

*The production was handled by North Market Street Graphics.*

*Printed and bound by R.R. Donnelley & Sons Company.*

McGraw-Hill books are available at special quality discounts to use as premiums and sales promotions, or for use in corporate training programs. For more information, please write to the Director of Special Sale, McGraw-Hill, 11 West 19th Street, New York, NY 10011. Or contact your local bookstore.

 This book is printed on recycled, acid-free paper containing a minimum of 50% recycled de-inked fiber.

# Contents

# Preface

Since the early 1970s, a great deal of time and energy has been spent in institutional, commercial and industrial facilities to reduce energy costs. Despite these efforts, a large amount of energy is wasted by the inefficient operation of energy-consuming devices.

Most people assume that standard operating and maintenance practices will ensure energy efficiency, but the truth is that very few facilities have processes in place to ensure energy-efficient operation. As a result, most facilities needlessly waste 10 to 25 percent of the energy they purchase.

This assertion is based upon the author's 20 years of experience in the field of building and industrial energy efficiency. That experience has consistently shown that far more resources have been expended in acquiring potentially more efficient equipment than have been expended in ensuring that all equipment, whether it be new or old, is operated efficiently.

There are two main reasons why processes focused on energy efficient operation are not commonly instituted in facilities: (1) there is a lack of information about the potential benefits, and (2) there are no procedural models to follow. The purpose of this book is to awaken facility managers to the energy cost savings potential of improving operating efficiency, and to provide a vision of how these activities should be structured.

Managers know that managing any activity requires the ability to define the desired outcome, measure the actual outcome and take appropriate action when desired and measured outcomes do not match up. They also know that management is not a project to be completed, but rather is an ongoing process to be sustained and improved upon over time.

This book asserts that achieving energy-efficient operation is a management issue. The desired operation of significant energy-consuming devices must be defined, the actual operation must be measured and deviations from desired operation must be acted upon in a timely manner. In addition, sustaining an efficient operation over time requires continuous, periodical repetition of this process. These activities should be a major component of any energy manager's job.

This book is written for managers who are responsible for the utility budget in their facilities, and for the people to whom they delegate responsibility for managing energy use and cost. Managers can gain an overview of the process by reading Chapters 1, 2 and 6, and can understand how the process is applied by reading Chapters 7, 8 and 9. The energy manager who will be responsible for setting up this process will find the necessary start-up activities described in Chapters 3, 4 and 5. Energy managers in industrial facilities or institutional facilities will find Chapter 9 helpful in adapting the efficient operation process to those properties.

The methods described in this book are most applicable to large energy consumers (facilities with energy costs of $250,000 or more per year). However, the general concepts can be scaled down and applied to facilities of any size.

The author sincerely hopes that the concepts and procedures set out in this book will help energy managers reduce energy costs, and reduce the needless waste of natural resources caused by the inefficient operation of energy-consuming devices in buildings.

# Acknowledgments

Some of the insights and experiences incorporated into this book were gained while participating in a research project conducted in the College of Architecture and Landscape Architecture in association with the Minnesota Building Research Center (MnBRC) at the University of Minnesota. The project was supported with funding from the U.S. Department of Energy administered through the Minnesota Department of Public Service.

A few individuals should be recognized for the significant contributions they have made to the creation of this book. John Carmody of the Minnesota Building Research Center at the University of Minnesota was a valuable collaborator throughout the process of developing this project. In addition to helping shape the book, John did the design and illustrations.

Professor Lance Lavine of the University of Minnesota College of Architecture and Landscape Architecture recognized the value of operating efficiency as a component of energy conservation in buildings. In collaboration with others at the Minnesota Building Research Center he created a research project that allowed the author to demonstrate and quantify the benefits of improving operating efficiency. He also urged the creation of this volume as a means of promoting energy-efficient operation in buildings.

I am also grateful to June Wheeler, my partner at Herzog/Wheeler & Associates, who contributed her energy management experience to this book and enthusiastically supported the considerable time that was expended in writing it. Donna Ahrens edited the final manuscript.

# CHAPTER 1

# Efficient Operation: The Missing Component of Energy Management

This chapter describes energy-efficient operation as one of the three basic components that should be included in any comprehensive process to minimize energy use and cost. This component can reduce energy costs by 10 to 25 percent at little or no capital cost. Most energy management programs are missing this component, thereby neglecting the most cost-effective opportunities to avoid energy costs.

## THREE COMPONENTS OF ENERGY MANAGEMENT

The following story introduces the three components of a comprehensive energy management process.

In 1974, an average American motorist experienced dramatic rises in the cost of gasoline for his family's car. In assessing the impact of this price increase, he noted that his family drove about 15,000 miles per year and remembered calculating the car's fuel efficiency to be approximately 15 miles per gallon. He quickly estimated that he currently was paying $500 to $700 more per year for gasoline than he had paid one year earlier.

He sat down with his wife to discuss their options for dealing with this unwelcome addition to the family expense budget. The first suggestion centered on where to buy their gasoline. The wife had observed a considerable price variation between gas stations, and she suggested that they seek out the lowest price rather than habitually purchasing gas from the same station.

Next, they decided to explore the wisdom of investing in a more fuel-efficient car. They began by checking out automobile advertisements in the newspaper and in magazines, as well as visiting a number of new car showrooms. Along the way, they learned of a number of investments they could make in their existing car that might improve its fuel efficiency, such as a new carburetor and radial tires. The husband agreed to be responsible for collecting information on the cost and savings potential of these options, but they both recognized that their current household budget had little room in it for a new, large expenditure.

Finally, just when they felt they had explored all of the options, the wife asked, "How do we know if our car is doing the best that it can? Forget about a new car, new carburetor or new tires—how do we know that our car, just as it is, is working to its maximum efficiency?" The husband replied that they didn't really know and admitted that paying more attention to issues like tire pressure, tune-ups and driving habits could increase mileage. After some reflection, he added, "We also don't really know if all of the driving we do is even necessary." They then discussed the prospects of carpooling, stopping for groceries on the way home from work instead of making a separate trip, and planning more efficiently the numerous trips to get the kids to and from school, Little League and swimming lessons.

After all of these discussions, the couple observed that they had identified three approaches to minimizing their gasoline expenses and agreed to do their best in all three areas. First, the wife agreed to watch gasoline prices to make sure they paid the lowest available price; second, the husband agreed to stay abreast of their options for replacing or upgrading their existing car; and third, they agreed to share the responsibility for making sure to operate their car as efficiently as possible, by planning the car use more carefully and keeping the car tuned. After some reflection, they concluded that even if they bought a new fuel-efficient car, they should always pay attention to gasoline prices and to the efficient operation of the new car.

As the story above illustrates, a comprehensive process for minimizing energy use and costs consists of ongoing involvement in the three fundamental components of energy management (see Figure 1-1):

- **Efficient purchasing:** This means purchasing energy at the lowest available unit cost.
- **Efficient operation:** This requires operating the equipment that consumes that energy as efficiently as possible.
- **Efficient equipment:** This entails upgrading or replacing existing equipment with more energy-efficient versions whenever it is cost effective.

Efficient purchasing and efficient operation should be the basic day-to-day activities of an energy management program. They entail the ongoing application of management skills and require little or no capital expenditure to achieve their goals.

The third component, making capital improvements, should support the first two by altering or replacing existing equipment in order to reduce costs or improve equipment efficiency. Unlike the first two components, upgrading existing equipment usually requires substantial capital investment to achieve its goal.

Most energy-efficiency programs concentrate their resources on equipment improvements first, when it would be more cost effective to begin with efficient purchasing and operation. In almost all facilities, the second component—operating existing equipment as efficiently as possible—is the least well understood and the most underdeveloped of the three. Ironically, this activity has a high potential for savings and requires little to no capital outlay.

The mission of this book is to provide energy managers with methods and instructions from which they can build a strong "efficient operation" component into their comprehensive energy management process.

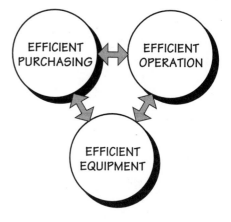

Figure 1-1. Three fundamental components of a comprehensive energy management process. Efficient operation is the focus of this book.

## WHAT IS ENERGY-EFFICIENT OPERATION?

Because the central theme of this entire book is "energy-efficient operation," it is prudent at this point to define what is meant by this term:

> *An energy-consuming device is operated efficiently when it consumes only as much energy as is necessary to fulfill its intended function.*

This definition is illustrated in the story above by the couple's realization that they would be operating their car efficiently only if they kept it well tuned and made no unnecessary trips.

Note that this definition focuses on two important questions. The first asks if the energy-consuming device is performing at its own optimal efficiency; the second asks if the work being done by the device is necessary to achieve the desired result.

In office buildings, for example, the function of air handlers is to provide thermal comfort and ventilation for building occupants. By our definition, such an air handler is operating efficiently if it stays well tuned (i.e., no malfunctions causing unnecessary heating or cooling) and if it operates only when necessary to meet the needs of the occupants (i.e., no unnecessary night and weekend operation).

## BENEFITS OF EFFICIENT OPERATION

The four main benefits of the efficient operation component are (1) substantial energy savings, (2) low cost, (3) no sacrifice of comfort or productivity, and (4) better information from which to make capital improvement decisions. Each of these is discussed briefly in the remainder of this section.

### Substantial Energy Savings

Ten to twenty-five percent of the energy currently used in commercial buildings for lighting, equipment and climate control could be saved with no adverse

Figure 1-2. Inefficient operation of existing equipment was adding 21 percent to this building's energy costs.

impacts on occupant comfort and without replacing existing building energy systems. Between 1989 and 1992 the author conducted a study of seven office buildings in Minneapolis, Minnesota. The study found that an average of 15.4 percent of the energy used for lighting, equipment and space conditioning could be saved simply by making energy-consuming equipment operate as it is expected to operate. The seven buildings represented a broad range of sizes (67,000 to 320,000 square feet) and mechanical systems. The building with the least potential to improve its energy performance could save 8 percent of its operating budget, or $39,000 annually in a 320,000-square-foot building. The building whose operation could be most improved could save 21 percent of its utility costs, or $13,000 annually in a 67,000-square-foot suburban office building.[1]

[1] Herzog, P., J. Wheeler, and L. Lavine. *Office Building Operations Case Study Reports.* University of Minnesota, 1992.

The savings resulting from improved operating efficiency in these seven buildings could be achieved by correcting relatively simple operating flaws. This did not require the correction of all operational errors, but only those that promised substantial enough savings to make this effort worthwhile.

The findings of this study are consistent with the author's 15 years of experience with improving the operating efficiency of a wide range of building systems and industrial processes. It is not at all uncommon to achieve a 20 percent savings simply by making the existing equipment operate more efficiently.

| Benefits for Building Owners |
| --- |
| • Substantial energy savings |
| • Low cost |
| • No sacrifice of comfort or productivity |
| • Better information from which to make capital improvement decisions |

## Low Cost

A fundamental characteristic of these savings is that they can be achieved with little or no capital outlay. Improved operating efficiency is based on a method of detecting and correcting energy-wasting malfunctions. This requires better-trained operating personnel and an allocation of time for them to detect and correct malfunctions, but it does not require any alteration to the systems themselves. The money spent to train personnel and implement this method normally is returned by the first year's energy savings. For example, the average annual savings resulting from improved operation in the seven office buildings mentioned above was $21,000. The cost of detecting these easily corrected malfunctions was approximately $10,000 per building.

## No Sacrifice of Occupant Comfort or Productivity

Previously in this chapter, an efficiently operating device was defined as one that "consumes only as much energy as is necessary to fulfill its intended function." This means using all the energy necessary to fully accomplish the desired task (light, heat, cool, ventilate, etc.), but it also means using only as much as is necessary and no more. Using this definition of operating efficiency ensures that there will never be any conflict between operating efficiency and occupant comfort, safety or productivity.

The potential for saving energy through improved operating efficiency, documented in the office building study cited earler, was completely within this definition of operating efficiency and in no way at odds with occupant comfort and productivity. One illustration of this is the fact that 68 percent of the energy waste caused by operating inefficiency was occurring during nights and weekends when the buildings were unoccupied. Correcting these malfunctions could not adversely effect occupants.

In another example, the author encountered resistance from the facility manager of a medical office building, who felt certain that any attempts to improve energy efficiency would result in an increase in complaints about comfort from the already-sensitive building occupants. Investigations were approved on the condition that no alterations would be made until the impact on occupants could be thoroughly discussed. One significant finding was a malfunctioning mixed air control that not only caused a great deal of unnecessary heating and cooling at the air handlers, but also explained why some units failed to keep the occupants cool in very hot weather. Correcting this operating malfunction saved the building $43,000 per year in energy costs and increased occupant comfort during the summer months.

These examples illustrate the very important fact that occupant satisfaction and/or a lack of comfort-related complaints do not necessarily indicate operating efficiency. Most facilities use 10 to 25 percent more energy than is necessary to meet occupant needs. By the above definition, the goal of operating efficiency is to find and eliminate any energy use that exceeds the amount necessary to meet the needs of the facility.

## Better Information from Which to Make Capital Improvement Decisions

Building owners, managers and operators who implement an efficient operation process will gain valuable knowledge and experience concerning their facilities' energy use patterns. They will know the actual energy use characteristics of the most significant energy-consuming devices, which will greatly enhance their ability to recognize the type of capital investments that would improve the facilities' energy efficiency. It will also provide a realistic basis on which to calculate the savings potential of improvement projects.

For example, an energy manager in a large commercial facility was contemplating completely replacing an eight-year-old HVAC control system based on the expectation of significant energy savings. However, when he carefully examined the operation of the existing controls, he found that substantial savings could be achieved simply by making the existing controls operate as intended.

After the necessary repairs and adjustments were made, the replacement project was reevaluated, comparing properly operating old controls to properly operating new controls. Based on this more realistic comparison, the total replacement could not be justified, and threfore the project scope was reduced to a much more cost-effective minor upgrade of selected control features.

Many energy-saving capital improvements fail to realize their expected savings because the expectations were based on assumptions about the needs served or the operating conditions of the existing equipment. Basing expectations on measured actual conditions can help energy managers avoid investing in improvements of marginal value. It also provides a measured "before" baseline to which "after" measurements can be compared to quantify the actual improvement achieved.

## BARRIERS TO ACHIEVING EFFICIENT BUILDING OPERATION

The goals of an efficient operation process are simple: to ensure that energy-consuming devices operate only when they need to, and to ensure that when they must operate, they do so efficiently. Despite the apparent simplicity of this activity, many energy consuming devices do not operate efficiently, and a significant amount of energy is constantly wasted in buildings and industrial processes. The fact that seemingly obvious and simple goals are not commonly achieved indicates that there are some barriers that must be overcome to achieve the desired outcome. The following paragraphs discuss the key obstacles to achieving and sustaining the efficient operation of buildings. *It should be noted that most of the barriers are managerial and organizational rather than technical.* This indicates that managers have a very important role to play in achieving operating efficiency.

## Potential for Savings Is Not Understood by Management

Managers of facilities and their superiors typically are not aware of the savings that could be achieved through improved operating efficiency of energy consuming equipment. They tend to assume that equipment is operating efficiently, and that this is the result of their routine operations and maintenance practices.

Managers must be open to the possibility that their operating and maintenance practices do not necessarily result in operating efficiency. The research and practical experience upon which this book is based shows that facilities can waste a significant portion of the energy they purchase unless they have a well-organized operating efficiency process. Management must initiate and support the processes described in this book in order to discover the potential for savings in their facilities. Once the savings potential is understood, energy managers can allocate the time and talent necessary to achieve and sustain these savings.

## Maintenance Procedures Are Not Designed to Achieve Operating Efficiency

One barrier to achieving operating efficiency is the failure to recognize that operating and maintenance procedures are designed primarily to achieve "complaint management" and secondarily to avoid premature or catastrophic failure of the equipment. Because operating staff performance is typically judged against these criteria, the staff's accountability, time and talents

> **Barriers to Achieving Efficient Operation**
>
> - Potential for savings is not understood by management.
> - Maintenance procedures are not designed to achieve operating efficiency.
> - Focus is on engineering projects rather than on a management process.
> - Management structure inhibits operating efficiency.
> - No methods are available for managing operating efficiency.

are devoted to achieving these two goals.

This situation can be illustrated by relating a discussion the author had with a building operator. His job performance was judged in part by a building survey, in which occupants were asked to evaluate their satisfaction with building comfort and the operating staff's attentiveness to their comfort needs.

The building operator was pleased to report a very significant increase in occupant satisfaction as measured by the survey. When asked how the improvement in his performance had been achieved, he reported, "I spend a lot of time walking around and talking to people." This operator had found a very effective method to achieve his objective of complaint management.

This true story illustrates the point that creative people will find ways to achieve goals if their goals are made explicit and measurable. Unfortunately, energy-efficient operation is not often an explicit goal, nor are there methods in place to make achievement of that goal measurable.

Operating staff rarely have a specific goal of sustaining operating efficiency. Furthermore, this requires additional activities not normally performed in facilities. Management must recognize the need to build this new capability into their facility management procedures.

## Focus Is on Engineering Projects Rather than on a Management Process

Another challenge to achieving operating efficiency is overcoming the tendency to focus all of the energy conservation effort on engineering projects while paying little or no attention to the process of achieving operating efficiency.

Energy conservation efforts generally begin with an energy audit conducted to identify cost-effective opportunities to improve the energy efficiency of the facility. These energy audits are typically performed by people who know both the expected efficiency of the existing equipment, and the expected efficiency of new, more energy-conserving equipment that could replace or enhance the performance of the existing devices. The

Figure 1-3. This office building could save $19,800 per year by eliminating the energy being wasted during the night and on weekends when the building is unoccupied.

energy auditors inventory the existing energy-consuming devices and then list alternative devices that are known to be more energy efficient. Energy auditors are usually engineering technicians who have a theoretical knowledge of energy-consuming devices but almost no access to knowledge about how these devices actually operate; therefore, they do not question whether the existing devices are operating as expected. All of these factors lead to a focus on capital improvement projects.

Another important contributor to the emphasis on equipment efficiency as opposed to operating efficiency is the fact that most information available about energy efficiency comes from vendors of energy-efficient equipment. They provide facility managers with an understanding of these replacement alternatives, but are not concerned with how efficiently the existing equipment is actually operating. All of these forces lead the facility manager to believe that the only avenue to improved energy efficiency is through capital improvement projects that might upgrade the efficiency of the equipment. There are few, if any, market forces that encourage the facility manager to ensure that the existing energy-consuming equipment, whether it be old or new, is actually operating at its expected level of efficiency.

## Management Structure Inhibits Operating Efficiency

Achieving operating efficiency is also complicated by the fact that most management structures inhibit the ability to achieve this goal. The following example illustrates this point.

An air-handling unit serves occupants in a specific area of a building. The time at which this unit needs to start in the morning may be determined by the earliest arriving occupants, and the time at which it can go off may be determined by the last worker leaving or by custodial staff. The necessary supply air temperature may be determined by the occupants in spaces with the most computers and other heat-generating office equipment, and the amount of air exhausted may be determined by kitchen staff who operate kitchen range and dishwasher exhaust hoods. The actual temperature within the air-handling unit may be established by a mechanical maintenance person, and the actual control sequence may be established by the person who programs the automated building control system. All of these people influence how the air-handling unit needs to operate or how it actually operates. They represent several departments and report to a variety of managers. This structure inhibits the ability to communicate effectively and to share goals and priorities.

Because the operation of energy-consuming equipment is a cross-functional activity, management must

devise methods to overcome the barriers posed by
normal departmental structures.

## No Methods Are Available for Managing Operating Efficiency

In addition to the barriers mentioned above, the
development of processes to achieve operating efficiency
have been inhibited by a lack of information on the
subject. Little has been written about methods, and
facility managers have no model upon which to con-
struct a process. This book provides such a model and
suggests general methods that can be adapted to specific
facilities and management structures.

# CHAPTER 2

# An Introduction to Energy-Efficient Building Operation

This chapter introduces an approach to achieving and sustaining energy-efficient building operation. Unlike most other approaches, which are engineering-oriented, this building operation model combines an understanding of the technical systems of the building with common sense management procedures. This chapter is divided into two parts: (1) a description of a step-by-step energy-efficient operation process, and (2) the role that management must play in order for this process to be successful. The energy-efficient operation process introduced in this chapter is described in detail in Chapters 3 through 6.

As an introduction to the process, the following story provides an analogy to the problems and solutions found in attempting to manage energy in commercial buildings.

A family consisting of a mother, father and six children uses the following system for managing its regular expenses: Each month the mother and father place a certain amount of cash in a kitchen drawer from which everyone in the family takes what he or she needs to meet regular expenses for food, clothing, entertainment, gas and oil for the car, etc. No one in the family has credit cards, and all transactions are on a cash basis.

When this system was first instituted, the cash drawer

occasionally became empty; when this happened, the person needing additional cash would complain to the parents, who would then contribute additional funds to the drawer. Over time, the parents learned how much cash was required each month, and complaints about lack of funds became less frequent. When complaints arose, adjustments were made in the quantity of cash contributed each month. The parents kept track of how much money was placed in the drawer on a monthly basis, and this amount was totalled annually. These records of monthly and total expenditures were occasionally reviewed, primarily for the purpose of budgeting the amount of cash that would be required in future months.

Upon returning from college, the oldest daughter, who had taken some courses in economics, asked her parents whether they thought their household was operated "economically" and whether the family's operating funds were being well managed. The parents asked the daughter to define what she meant by "economical." After some discussion, they agreed that a family member would be making an economical expenditure if the purchase had the following characteristics: the purchase stemmed from a legitimate need, and the item purchased was the best available value.

The daughter and her parents generally agreed that their household funds would be well managed if sufficient funds were provided to meet the family's requirements and these funds were used economically, according to their agreed-upon definition.

The daughter asked her father how they might be able to determine if their household was economical and well managed. The father replied that he knew that the quantity of funds provided was sufficient because there were no complaints of insufficient cash. He also noted that there were no obvious signs of extravagance and added that conversations with friends and co-workers indicated that their family expenses were generally in line with those of other families of similar size.

The daughter pointed out that the three indicators her father mentioned—lack of complaint, lack of obvious extravagance and conformity to families of similar size—

are not very good indicators of economical behavior as previously defined. None of them directly addresses the question: Do we spend *only* as much as is necessary to meet our needs?

The daughter suggested that each purchase in the household should be reviewed and the following questions asked:

- Is this expenditure necessary?
- How much should we be paying for this item?
- How much do we pay for this item?

While the parents agreed that these questions would lead to the economical use of the family funds, they felt that it would take a great deal of time and effort to ask them of every purchase and expressed doubt that this effort would be worthwhile. They all agreed that this level of scrutiny would not be warranted for every purchase, but that it might be worthwhile for large purchases and for regular recurring purchases that accounted for a significant portion of their total expenditures.

The daughter suggested that they start by having each person in the household write down the amount he or she removed from the drawer. She volunteered to work with the person with the largest expenditure at the end of a month to help that person break down the total amount spent into categories such as food, clothing, entertainment, transportation, etc. As it gradually became clear which purchases consumed the most money, she would work with each purchaser to review the actual needs the purchase was intended to satisfy, determine how much it should cost to satisfy that need, and how much was actually spent to satisfy that need.

The parents thought their daughter's idea of focusing on the largest expenditures was a good one, but they continued to be skeptical about whether this effort would be worthwhile. When asked what she believed the benefits would be, the daughter answered that studies she had read at school indicated that 10 to 25 percent of the money spent for family expenses could be saved if the family had an orderly process to ensure economical behavior. The parents noted that they put approximately $20,000 per year in the kitchen drawer, and agreed that a savings of $2,000 to $5,000 would certainly justify some effort to manage those expenditures better.

The parents encouraged the daughter to begin her efforts. They could see the benefits of knowing where the dollars they were contributing to the kitchen drawer were actually being spent, and they looked forward to the prospect of a family vacation being funded by the savings achieved.

———————

The methods used to manage energy expenditures in both facilities and industrial processes are very similar to those illustrated in this story. Paying the monthly utility bill is very much like the parents' making monthly contributions to the cash drawer in the story. Additions to the amount of money in the drawer are akin to the energy use capacity of facilities where more energy is provided when complaints indicate that more energy is required.

Figure 2-1. In most buildings, the majority of the energy-consuming devices do not have processes in place to ensure that they operate efficiently.

As in the story, most facilities have very little documentation to account for where the energy is being "spent." When asked, most people have some opinion about where the major energy expenditures are, but these opinions are rarely verified by measurement or documentation.

Like the parents in the story, facility managers and operators judge the efficiency of their operation by its lack of complaints, the absence of outward signs of extravagant energy use and, occasionally, by comparing their facility to other similar facilities. A lack of complaint is viewed as an indication that enough is being provided; a lack of evidence of extravagance is seen simply as an indication that the use is not exorbitant. Yet, as in the story, neither of these conditions indicates whether or not the use is truly "economical." And like the family comparing its expenditures to expenditures of similar families, comparisons of energy use in similar facilities provide only the most general comparative information. They shed almost no light on the relationship between the amount of energy a facility actually uses and the amount of energy that it needs to use.

The prospect of evaluating the actual and required energy used by every energy-consuming device appears as tedious as tracking every expense in a family budget. However, the approach suggested in the story is equally valid for managing energy costs. A procedure that methodically begins to track where the energy dollars are spent and focuses attention on the largest users will make the process less time consuming and more cost effective.

As in the story above, studies have indicated that a reduction of 10 to 25 percent in energy use can be achieved in most facilities by asking the major energy users the same three questions:

- What is the need this energy-consuming device serves?

- How much energy does it use to fill that need?

- How much energy *should* it use to fill that need?

Experience with this process shows that it often uncovers opportunities to reduce energy use. Sometimes energy is provided that is not needed (e.g., lights burning in empty spaces, heating and cooling of unoccupied buildings), and sometimes the amount of energy consumed to provide a legitimate need exceeds the amount required to fill that need (e.g., simultaneous heating and cooling, excessive equipment cycling, control malfunctions, etc.)

In the story above, the family could choose to continue operating by its old methods and accept the fact that it was wasting operating funds because of inefficiencies in its purchasing methods. Similarly, facilities and industrial processes that do not have an orderly method of "managing" the energy consumed by their largest energy users must accept that 10 to 25 percent of their energy dollars are being wasted.

## KEY CONCEPTS OF ENERGY-EFFICIENT BUILDING OPERATION

The remainder of this book describes a process for achieving operating efficiency. This process is based on the following key concepts: (1) it assigns an explicit accountability for operating efficiency, (2) it involves the people who influence operations, (3) it is designed as an ongoing process, (4) it is based upon actual measurement of energy use patterns, and (5) it is designed to be cost effective. The following paragraphs elaborate on these concepts.

### Assign an Accountability for Operating Efficiency

As previously noted, most facilities have operators responsible for minimizing comfort- or productivity-related complaints, and many have engineers responsible for implementing cost-effective equipment upgrades. However, seldom is anyone assigned the responsibility for operating existing equipment to its optimum energy efficiency. The process described in this book creates a

---

**Key Concepts of Efficient Building Operation**

- Assign an accountability for operating efficiency.

- Involve the people who influence operation.

- Institute an ongoing process.

- Measure actual energy use patterns.

- Ensure that efforts are cost effective.

structure for assigning this responsibility to the people who have the most effect on equipment operation.

### Involve the People Who Influence Operation

The previous chapter described how typical management structure inhibits the ability to involve all of the key people who influence the operation of energy-consuming equipment.

Operating efficiency generally is the responsibility of someone who has almost no ability to control it. For example, the responsibility for eliminating energy waste is often accepted by an energy manager who attempts to minimize unnecessary lighting or equipment operation through the use of signs, stickers and other "awareness" efforts. These activities have marginal impact because they fail to place responsibility with the true "operators" of the equipment.

The true "operators" of energy-consuming devices are numerous and varied, but they all must participate in making the equipment they influence operate efficiently. The process described in the following chapters provides methods for identifying and involving the key people who influence operation.

### Institute an Ongoing Process

Operating efficiency is not a problem to be solved, but rather a set of variables to be managed. A facility's need for energy varies over time, as does the ability of the energy-consuming devices to supply those needs efficiently. Therefore, achieving operating efficiency cannot be viewed as a one-time project, but instead must be structured as an ongoing management process.

The procedure described in this book consists of an ongoing cyclical process of measuring actual operating patterns, comparing them to required operating patterns, and minimizing any significant waste detected. The structuring of this approach as a management process, rather than an engineering project, is absolutely essential to achieving and sustaining operating efficiency.

## Measure Actual Energy Use Patterns

In order for building operations to be made manageable, they must be made measurable. Operating efficiency is achieved when the amount of energy actually used by a device closely matches the amount that device requires to perform its intended function. To determine if an energy-consuming device is operating efficiently or wastefully, its actual energy use must be measurable by methods that are affordable and technologically accessible to the average building operator.

It is also important to note that the quantity of energy used by a device is a function of its rate of energy consumption and of the time during which it operates. Therefore, a measurement of energy cannot be a momentary measurement of rate, but rather must be a profile of rate over time.

Recent advances in datalogging technology have revolutionized operating efficiency management by making measurements of energy rate over time both affordable and technologically accessible to the average building operator. The procedures described in this book are based on the use of small, portable datalogging equipment capable of measuring temperatures, humidity and electrical current. These devices are unobtrusive, easy to install and easily placed where they can detect wasteful operation. Many of the measurements required in this process can also be performed by using the trendlogging capability of the energy management systems that are already installed in many facilities.

## Ensure That Efforts Are Cost Effective

The cost effectiveness of this efficient operation process depends upon proportioning the effort expended on each energy consumer according to its contribution to the facility's total annual energy cost. Following this procedure, the efficiency management process begins with the largest and most costly energy-consuming equipment and ensures that it is operating efficiently before proceeding to equipment that is less costly to operate.

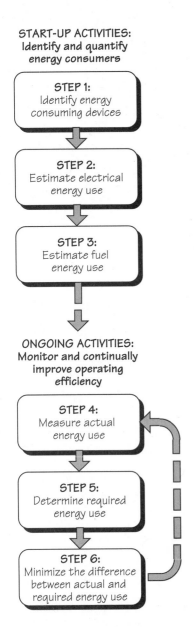

Figure 2-2. Steps required in the energy-efficient building operation process.

In most facilities, 75 to 80 percent of the annual energy cost is incurred by the five or six largest energy-consuming devices or systems. This situation simplifies the efficient operation process by focusing attention on the largest devices, where energy wasting malfunctions can be the most costly.

Many smaller systems can waste energy and therefore can yield savings opportunities. The cost effectiveness of managing these systems can be assured if the energy manager regularly monitors the savings achieved and compares them to the effort expended.

## THE PROCESS FOR ACHIEVING ENERGY-EFFICIENT BUILDING OPERATION

The process for achieving and sustaining energy-efficient operation is comprised of two main parts: (1) start-up activities, and (2) ongoing activities.

The first part consists of the start-up activities shown at the top of Figure 2-2. These activities are similar to the part in the story where the daughter begins to trace where the money goes after being taken from the drawer, in order to determine which expenditures were large enough to warrant examination. The goal of these first three steps is to identify where the energy dollars flow, so that the efforts to achieve operating efficiency can be focused on the most costly consumers.

The second part consists of three ongoing activities, the goal of which is to ensure that the most costly items identified in the start-up tasks are always operated as efficiently as possible. These activities are like the daughter's plan in the story in that they involve periodic examination of each large expenditure to determine whether the funds are being used economically.

## START-UP ACTIVITIES
## Identifying and Quantifying Energy Consumers

### Step 1: Identify energy-consuming devices

The first step of the process is to inventory the existing devices and systems that consume energy in the building. The energy manager should tour the building to trace energy flow paths and to make a list of the energy-consuming devices and systems (see Figure 2-3). Drawings and specifications for the building should then be collected, and schematic drawings prepared that illustrate the energy flows and relationships in the building systems. Finally, it is important to create an energy management filing system for all the information that will be collected and maintained. Each of these tasks is described in detail in Chapter 3.

```
ELECTRICAL ENERGY USES
Elevators
Lighting
Office equipment
Air compressor
Pumps
Exhaust fans
Cooling
Air handling

FUEL ENERGY USES
Domestic hot water
Unit heaters
Perimeter radiation
Reheat
```

Figure 2-3. This list of energy-consuming devices is a typical example of a list compiled during Step 1.

### Step 2: Estimate electrical energy use

The second step involves devoting a limited amount of effort to make rough estimates of how much electrical energy is used for each major device or system listed in Step 1. This is done by assembling electric utility bill information and then gathering information on operating schedules. Based on various simple take-off methods and estimating procedures, the annual use of each device or system can then be estimated with sufficient accuracy. This is usually done by first allocating costs to constant (non-weather-related) uses and then allocating the remainder of the cost to variable (weather-related) uses. Finally, a total annual electric use allocation can be portrayed in the form of a bar chart to quickly see the most significant systems (see Figure 2-4). Each of these tasks is described in detail in Chapter 4.

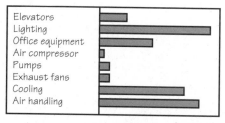

Figure 2-4. In Step 2, rough estimates of electrical energy use are made and plotted on a bar graph to discover the largest energy users.

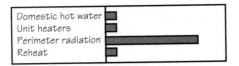

Figure 2-5. In Step 3, rough estimates of fuel energy use are made and plotted on a bar graph to discover the largest energy users.

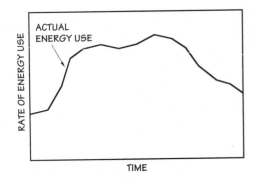

Figure 2-6. The actual energy use profile is determined in Step 4. Based on measurements of actual energy use, a graph of energy use over time is created.

## Step 3: Estimate fuel energy use

The third step is identical to the second step, except that it addresses fuel-consuming rather than electricity-consuming equipment. As with electrical use, allocations are developed by first assembling fuel utility bill information and then gathering information on operating schedules. Based on various simple take-off methods and estimating procedures, the annual use of each device or system can then be estimated with sufficient accuracy. This is usually done by first allocating costs to constant (non-weather-related) uses and then allocating the remainder of the cost to variable (weather-related) uses. Finally, a total annual fuel use allocation can be portrayed in the form of a bar chart to quickly see the most significant systems (see Figure 2-5). Each of these tasks is described in detail in Chapter 5.

## ONGOING ACTIVITIES:
## Monitoring and Continually Improving Operating Efficiency

### Step 4: Measure actual energy use

Based on the allocation of energy use from the previous steps, it is possible to determine which systems use the most energy and thus have the greatest potential for savings. The largest energy users are measured first. Measuring the actual performance of energy-consuming devices and systems is the basis for discovering inefficiencies and then correcting them. To manage energy use, a measurement of rate of use over time must be created (see Figure 2-6). Measuring tools such as portable dataloggers can be used to achieve convenient, accurate and relatively low-cost measurements.

## Step 5: Determine required energy use

After examining the actual energy use profiles created in the previous step, the energy manager works with the people who operate the eqipment measured in step 4 to develop a required energy use profile (see Figure 2-7). This required profile is based on a common sense analysis of the actual needs the devices is intended to meet. Developing the required profile reveals waste occurring either because of system malfunctions or because systems are operating when they are not required.

## Step 6: Minimize the difference between actual and required energy use

The final step in the process is intended to minimize any significant differences between the actual energy use of any device or system and its required use. To accomplish this, the energy manager and the equipment operators estimate the savings potential, list options for achieving savings, implement these actions and then remeasure to verify that efficient operation has been achieved (see Figure 2-8).

The last three steps are repeated periodically to assure that savings are maintained, to reveal further savings and, when appropriate, to respond to new conditions. Since Steps 4, 5 and 6 are closely linked and represent a continuous, repeated process, they are described in detail together in Chapter 6. The application of these three ongoing activities is illustrated by examples in Chapters 7 and 8.

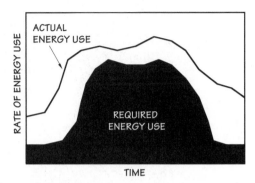

Figure 2-7. In Step 5, the required energy use profile is plotted over the actual use. The area between the two lines represents wasted energy.

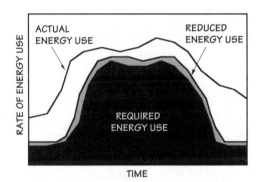

Figure 2-8. In Step 6, wasteful energy use patterns have been identified and corrected. The result is a reduction in the actual energy use, but there has been no sacrifice in terms of meeting required energy needs.

## THE ROLE OF MANAGEMENT

In order for the efficient operation process to be effective, the management team of an organization or institution must establish certain policies, responsibilities and attitudes, described below.

**1. Value energy-efficient operation.**

Management must value the elimination of unnecessary energy use and cost, as well as the resulting environmental degradation.

**2. Develop enthusiastic participation.**

Management must have the ability to ensure the enthusiastic participation of the persons whose involvement is essential. It is critical to the success of this effort that management look at the accountability, incentives and motivation of all key participants to ensure that there are no barriers to their wholehearted participation.

One common barrier to the enthusiastic participation of operating personnel is the perception that the identification of energy wasting malfunctions will reflect poorly on their past performance. Management must recognize that operating personnel typically focus their efforts on managing occupant complaints and maintaining equipment, and that the proactive task of discovering energy-wasting malfunctions is over and above their normal activities. Management must establish this premise with operating personnel, and convince them that the discovery and correction of energy-wasting malfunctions will be looked upon as a positive contribution rather than as an indictment of previous efforts.

**3. Recognize cross-functional nature of effort.**

Management must recognize the cross-functional nature of this effort, as illustrated by the following example. While working in laboratory facilities, the author has observed that the accountability for

---

**Key Management Actions and Policies**

1. Value energy-efficient operation.

2. Develop enthusiastic participation.

3. Recognize cross-functional nature of effort.

4. Define return on investment.

5. Institute methods of accounting.

6. Designate a start-up leader.

7. Recognize needs during start-up phase.

energy costs is typically assigned to the facilities staff, and that laboratory hood exhaust is one of the major contributors to energy costs. Facilities staff are often frustrated in their energy conservation efforts by the tendency of laboratory personnel to leave lab hoods open unnecessarily, especially during nights and weekends. The essence of the problem is that the group accountable for energy use does not include the true "operators" of the most energy-intensive equipment.

This process requires the formation of an *energy management team* that can occasionally involve all of the people who significantly influence the energy use of the equipment under study. This team will include personnel representing electrical maintenance; HVAC maintenance; contract maintenance; custodians; security staff; food service staff; occupants of energy intensive spaces such as computer rooms, clean rooms and laboratories; and occupants of general office spaces. This need for cross-functional participation requires that the management commitment be at a high enough level to ensure the involvement of all the key people.

4. **Define return on investment.**

Management should define an acceptable return on the investment in the energy reduction program. For example, management might stipulate that each dollar spent on this effort should return $1.20 in avoided energy costs.

5. **Institute methods of accounting.**

Management must work with the energy team to institute simple methods to account for the time and materials invested in the efficient operation program. This is necessary to ensure that the appropriate relationship between investment and return is maintained. This accounting should recognize that the initial start-up of the process will take considerably more time than will be required for maintenance of the mature process.

## 6. Designate a start-up leader.

An appropriate start-up leader must be designated. The person to lead the start-up process should be selected with the following in mind: While the use of energy by mechanical devices involves technical issues, the establishment of an orderly, methodical management process is much more an organizational task than it is a technical one. The appropriate person will be skilled in collecting information, organizing procedures, keeping records, chairing informal team meetings and communicating with persons of diverse skills and backgrounds.

It should be recognized that people with good "start-up" skills may not be the best people to sustain the process once it has been established. It is highly likely that the responsibility for the maintenance of the ongoing process may be handed off to another team member once its procedures and responsibilities are clearly established.

## 7. Recognize needs during start-up phase.

Management must recognize that the start-up phase activities will require a concentrated effort, after which the cyclical repetition of the process will be much less demanding.

# CHAPTER 3

# Identifying Energy-Consuming Devices

Chapter 2 presented an energy-efficient operation process and a discussion of the role that management must play in order for this process to be successful. The process includes six steps—three start-up steps designed to determine the areas of greatest potential savings, followed by a three-step ongoing process to monitor and improve operating efficiency. This chapter describes the first start-up step of the process—identifying the energy-consuming devices and systems in a building (Figure 3-1).

Purchased energy in buildings can be accounted for in two places: (1) the location where the energy is input into each energy-consuming site, and (2) the place where that same energy leaves the building (the energy loss site). An example of accounting for energy in the first method would be to measure the fuel consumed by a boiler used to heat a building in a cold climate. Applying the second method to the same example would involve accounting for the heat lost through the roof, walls, windows and other components of the building envelope.

The methods described in this book focus on accounting for energy use at input sites, for several reasons. First, energy input sites are far more measurable than loss sites. The fuel input into a boiler can be measured far more easily than the heat loss through all the components of a building envelope.

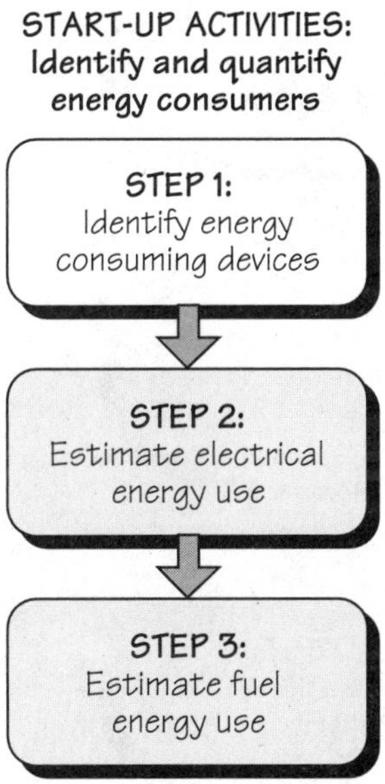

**START-UP ACTIVITIES:**
Identify and quantify
energy consumers

**STEP 1:**
Identify energy
consuming devices

**STEP 2:**
Estimate electrical
energy use

**STEP 3:**
Estimate fuel
energy use

Figure 3-1. This chapter describes the first step of the energy-efficient operation process.

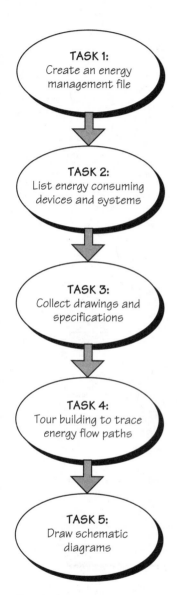

Figure 3-2. Tasks included in Step 1 of the energy-efficient operation procedure.

Another reason to focus on input sites is that they have operating variables that can dramatically alter the efficiency of their performance. For example, the efficiency of converting fuel to useful heat in a boiler can change by 10 percent or more over a rather short period of time, depending on how the boiler is maintained and operated. However, a building envelope's resistance to heat flow will change little over time, has no operating variables and is only marginally influenced by day-to-day maintenance procedures.

For these two main reasons, it is advantageous to manage the energy-efficient behavior at the input sites rather than at the sites where energy is lost. Improving a thermally inefficient envelope is a capital improvement project to be pursued only after all efforts at efficient operation have been implemented.

The first start-up activity required for a specific facility is to identify that facility's unique energy-consuming devices and systems (input sites). The tasks described in this chapter are designed to achieve that purpose (see Figure 3-2).

## TASK 1: CREATE AN ENERGY MANAGEMENT FILE

*Good management requires good information*

During the start-up phase of the energy-efficient operation process, a great deal of diverse information will be collected that will form the foundation for the ongoing process. This will include information on how much of each type of energy is purchased, where it goes and how the actual behavior of each energy-using device compares with that device's expected behavior. Considerable effort will be expended in collecting these data, but this effort could be wasted unless the information is stored in a file from which it can be easily retrieved.

Sustaining energy-efficient operation is a process that will require periodic attention for as long as the facility purchases and uses energy. However, after the start-up phase, it will be a part-time task for the participants who will perform the work at intervals appropriate to their facility's needs. This process of setting aside and restarting a management process can be very inefficient unless the essential records of the process are sufficiently well organized to allow the participants to quickly pick up where they left off.

The file outline suggested in this section is based upon the author's extensive experience in creating energy management process files for numerous commercial and industrial facilities. A file drawer or a loose-leaf three-ring binder, organized with tabs similar to those shown in Figure 3-3, will be invaluable in achieving the record storage needs. The major and minor tabs of the energy management file are briefly discussed below. Chapters 4 through 8 provide a detailed description of the data to be collected and where they are to be stored.

The energy management file is divided into two or more major sections. Section A (Administration) contains general information about the process, its participants, records of their activities and general information about the energy-consuming characteristics of the facility in total. Section B contains specific information about the devices that consume electrical energy and their performance characteristics. More sections are added for each additional metered source of energy. In most buildings, a Section C would be added to contain information about devices that consume fuels. For example, Section C would be titled *Steam* in the case of buildings that purchase steam as a heating source instead of fuels. An additional Section D would be added to accommodate a building that purchases chilled water as a cooling source.

The following paragraphs introduce the structure of the file. Detailed information on the file content and how to collect it follows in this chapter and subsequent chapters.

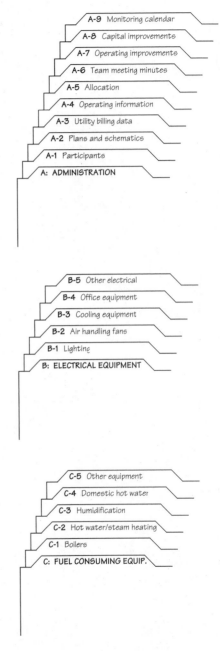

Figure 3-3. Tabs for energy management filing system.

## Section A - Administration

### Tab A-1 Participants

Names, addresses and phone numbers of key persons who affect energy use (e.g., building operator, custodial and security staff representatives, outside contractors who maintain energy-consuming equipment, managers who support the energy effort, facility administrator, utility account representative, etc.).

### Tab A-2 Plans and Schematic Drawings

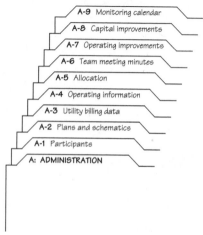

Key diagrammatic documents that describe the building and its energy-consuming systems.

### Tab A-3 Utility Meter/Billing Data

Historical records of energy use and costs.

### Tab A-4 Operating Information

Records of times that energy-consuming devices are expected to operate and the conditions (set points) they are expected to achieve.

### Tab A-5 Allocation

Documents showing how total purchased energy is distributed among the various energy-consuming devices. (Chapters 4 and 5 explain how to allocate energy use.)

### Tab A-6 Team Meeting Minutes

Records of the discussions and actions taken by the energy management team.

### Tab A-7 Operating Improvements

A list of operating improvement opportunities and a log of actions completed and savings achieved.

Figure 3-4. Tabs for the Administration section of the filing system.

*Tab A-8  Capital Improvements*

A list of opportunities for energy-saving capital improvement and a log of improvements made and savings achieved.

*Tab A-9  Monitoring Calendar*

A calendar showing the ongoing periodic monitoring that the energy management team has decided is necessary to ensure the efficient operation of the most significant energy-consuming equipment.

## Section B - Electrical Equipment

This section will contain a tab for each major category of electricity-consuming device, such as lighting, office equipment, air handlers, chillers, pumps and elevators. Each tab should contain information that describes the device or system and information about its expected operation, as well as data from measurements of its actual operation.  Examples of tabs typically found in Section B for an office building energy management file are shown in Figure 3-3.

Some categories of electrical equipment will be further subdivided into subcategories representing the various points at which measurements are taken.  For example, if the lighting in a building is measured at three lighting panel locations, a subtab would be created for each panel in order to file the measurements and other relevant information (see Figure 3-5).

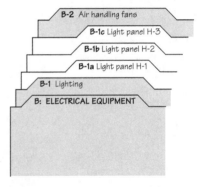

Figure 3-5. Subtabs for electric lighting section of filing system.

## Section C - Fuel-Consuming Equipment

This section will contain a tab for each category of devices that consume fuel energy.  Each tab will contain information about the devices, how they are intended to operate and measurements of how they actually operate. Examples of Section C tabs for a typical office building are found in Figure 3-3.

As in Section B above, some or all categories of fuel-consuming equipment will need to be further divided

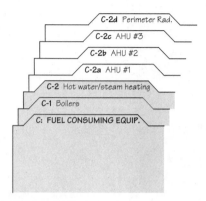

Figure 3-6. Subtabs for hot water heating section of filing system.

---

**Electrical Use**

Lighting
Office equipment
Air-handler fans
Cooling equipment
Elevators
Exhaust fans
Pumps
Other electrical

**Fuel Use**

Boilers/perimeter radiation
Domestic hot water

---

Figure 3-7. List of typical energy-consuming devices.

into subcategories. For example, the hot water system (Tab C-2) may consist of heating coils inside of three air-handler units plus a perimeter radiation system. Sub-tabs should be created to file measurements and other information for each significant device or system that consumes energy for hot water heating (see Figure 3-6).

## TASK 2: LIST ENERGY-CONSUMING DEVICES AND SYSTEMS

The objective of this task is to prepare a list of the facility's energy consumers. This list, similar to Figure 3-7, will become the subtabs in section B and C of the file. The list should consist of categories of energy consumers rather than a detailed list that includes every energy-consuming device. For example, "lighting" will be a single entry on this list, despite the likelihood that the building contains several types of lighting: overhead lights, task lighting, exterior lighting, etc. (a more de-tailed listing of the devices in each category is explained in Chapters 4 and 5). A review of the entries in the sample list shows that almost all of the categories may represent multiple devices. These categories correspond to the tabs in the Electrical and Fuel sections of the energy management file.

The list should have a major section for each source of billed energy. Most buildings will require one section of the list for electrical energy plus one for fuels (usually natural gas). In facilities where more than one fuel flows through the same input path, such as dual-fueled boil-ers, only one major section is required. Buildings that purchase steam, hot water or chilled water should have a major section for each separately metered energy source.

If the utility meter is conceived as the trunk of a tree through which the water and nutrients must flow, this activity identifies the branches of the tree. Chapters 4 and 5, explain how to determine which branches are the largest and which are the smallest. Once the energy manager knows where the energy flows and which branches receive the most, it will be easy to decide which branches should receive the highest priority in the energy management effort.

At this stage, the lists should be considered preliminary and subject to editing as more information is collected. It is not important that every energy consumer be listed because many are too small to warrant a great deal of attention. It is probable that the largest five or six items on each list will account for more than 90 percent of the total energy use. These are the items where the efficient operation process will be most beneficial.

## TASK 3: COLLECT AND REVIEW DRAWINGS AND SPECIFICATIONS

The first task in identifying energy-consuming devices and systems is to assemble and review any available documents that describe them. The most comprehensive source of this information usually is the drawings and specifications from which the facility was originally constructed. An even better source, if available, is as-built drawings that are the original drawings and specifications, edited to reflect any subsequent changes made to the facility.

Only a small portion of the information contained in building drawings and specifications is referred to regularly in the energy-efficient operation process. Once this key information is located, it should be photocopied (and reduced if necessary) for inclusion in the energy management file. Experience has shown that using the drawing and specification documents in their entirety as a reference for the energy-efficient operation process will result in countless frustrating hours searching anew for information previously located. Information captured on 8-1/2 x 11 sheets is not only easily filed, but also can be readily copied or made into transparencies for group discussion.

Drawings that would become unreadable if reduced should be copied full size and kept with the energy management file, and a sheet describing the drawing's content and location should be placed in Section A—Tab 2 (Figure 3-8).

Section A: Administration

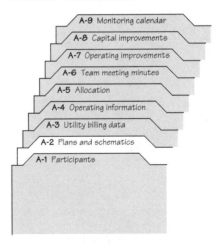

Figure 3-8. Place drawings into Section A—Tab 2 of the filing system.

## Architectural Drawings

Architectural drawings seldom show any energy input sites. However, architectural floor plans and full building sections will give an image of the general configuration of the building. The floor plan and elevation of a typical four-story office building are shown in Figure 3-9. This example will be used in this chapter to illustrate the energy-efficient operation process. A knowledge of the building configuration and how it is laid out on the architectural plans will assist in understanding the mechanical and electrical plans. These typically consist of the same architectural plans with the energy-consuming mechanical and electrical equipment superimposed upon them.

It is strongly recommended that small (8-1/2 x 11), simplified floor plans of the facility be acquired at this time. In addition to facilitating discussion about the location of energy management activities within the

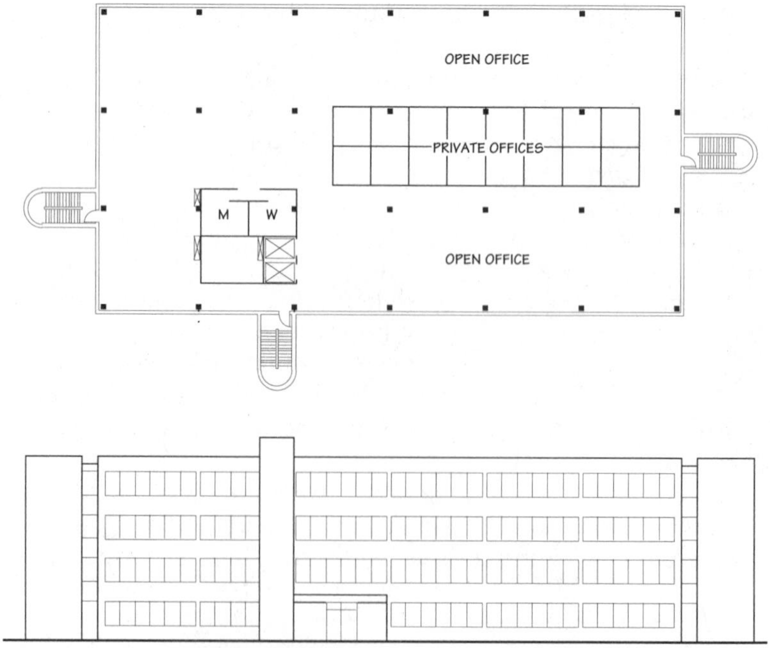

Figure 3-9. Floor plan and elevation of a typical four-story office building. This building will be used to illustrate the energy-efficient operation process.

building, copies of these plans are useful for recording information about the location of key energy-consuming equipment. The plans can be produced quickly by tracing the outline of a reduced architectural plan and may already exist in the form of plans that show the location of building exits and fire safety equipment. A single plan may be sufficient in a multi-story building where all of the floors are nearly identical.

A building elevation or section is useful to describe the number and relationship of levels in complex multi-floor buildings. The collected drawings should be filed in Section A—Tab 2 of the energy management file.

## Mechanical Drawings and Specifications

Mechanical floor plans will show how heating, ventilating and air conditioning (HVAC) is distributed in the building, and the location of the equipment that provides it. A list of all the building's air-handling units will be found in the *Schedules* section of the mechanical drawings or specifications. A copy of this schedule should be made for Section B—Tab 2 of the energy management file (Figure 3-10).

In the case of buildings with water-to-air heat pumps, the mechanical plan will show the number and location of heat pumps. A chart listing all heat pumps, along with their sizes and capacities, will usually be found in the *Schedules* of the drawings or specifications and should also be copied for the energy management file.

The *Schedules* section of the mechanical drawings or specifications should be studied for lists of additional energy-consuming equipment, such as boilers, chillers, cooling towers, water heaters, pumps and exhaust fans. The location of this equipment will be shown on the enlarged plans of mechanical equipment rooms. This information should be reviewed and filed for future reference in the front of Section B if the equipment consumes electrical energy, or in Section C if it primarily consumes fuel energy (Figure 3-11). When the energy-efficient operation process is set up, much of this information will be distributed to the appropriate subtabs in the electrical or fuels sections of the filing system.

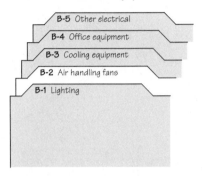

Section B: Electrical equipment

B-5 Other electrical
B-4 Office equipment
B-3 Cooling equipment
B-2 Air handling fans
B-1 Lighting

Figure 3-10. Place schedules for air handling units into Section B—Tab 2 of the filing system.

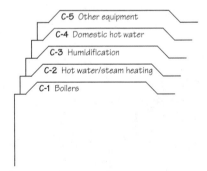

Section C: Fuel consuming equipment

C-5 Other equipment
C-4 Domestic hot water
C-3 Humidification
C-2 Hot water/steam heating
C-1 Boilers

Figure 3-11. Place schedules for fuel consuming equipment into the appropriate tabs in Section C of the filing system.

Figure 3-12. Electrical riser diagram.

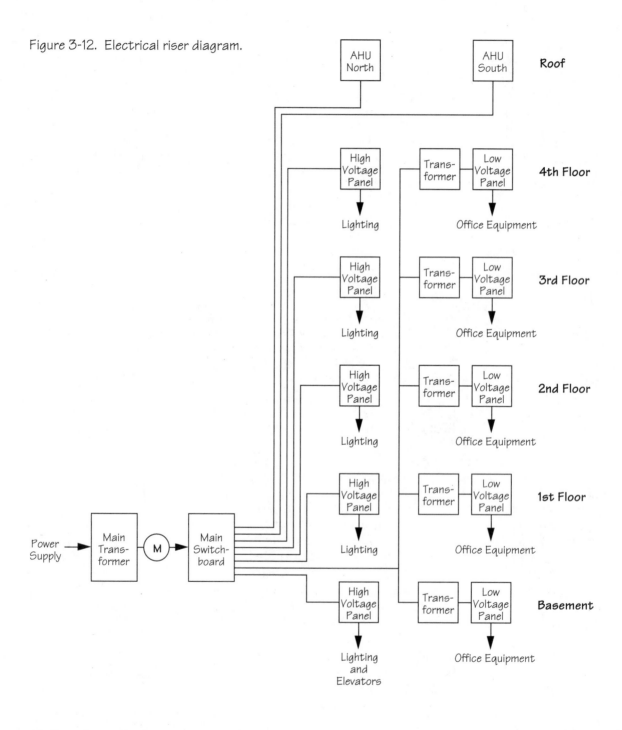

## Electrical Drawings and Specifications

The electrical drawings will have lighting plans that show the number and location of light fixtures, and light fixture schedules that describe the types and sizes of fixtures. This information should be kept available for estimating lighting energy, as described in Chapter 4. However, it may not be of sufficient long-term value to warrant inclusion in the file.

Electrical drawings typically contain an electrical riser diagram similar to that shown in Figure 3-12. This diagram is very useful in managing building electrical use because it describes the path of electrical flow from the point at which it enters the building to the significant electrical energy input sites. Once this diagram is understood, it will provide insight into the locations where measurements will show the actual use of energy by the various electricity-consuming systems. A copy of the electrical riser diagram should be filed in Section A—Tab 2 of the energy management file (Figure 3-13).

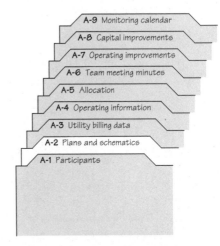

Section A: Administration

A-9 Monitoring calendar
A-8 Capital improvements
A-7 Operating improvements
A-6 Team meeting minutes
A-5 Allocation
A-4 Operating information
A-3 Utility billing data
A-2 Plans and schematics
A-1 Participants

Figure 3-13. Place electrical riser diagram into Section A—Tab 2 of the filing system.

---

### CHECKLIST OF ITEMS TO COLLECT

**1. Architectural drawings**

- floor plans
- building sections and elevations

**2. Mechanical drawings and specifications**

- plans showing equipment and the corresponding areas served
- plans of mechanical equipment rooms showing major equipment
- schedule listing energy-consuming equipment

**3. Electrical drawings and specifications**

- plan showing lighting system
- schedules listing lighting equipment sizes and types
- schedule listing electricity- consuming equipment— electric motors
- electrical riser diagram

**Section B: Electrical equipment**

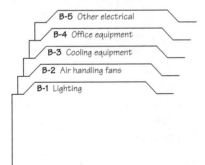

Figure 3-14. Place schedules for electrical equipment into the appropriate tabs in Section B of the filing system.

The electrical drawings will also have a *Schedules* section, which should be studied for lists of electricity-consuming equipment, such as electric motors that drive pumps, air handler fans, exhaust fans, compressors and elevators, as well as electrical resistance heaters, boilers, water heaters and space heaters. Copies of these schedules should be placed in the front of each appropriate tab in Section B of the filing system (Figure 3-14).

## TASK 4: TOUR BUILDING TO TRACE ENERGY FLOW PATHS

At this stage, the person responsible for the set-up phase of the energy-efficient operation process (referred to hereafter as the energy manager) should tour the facility. The objective is to trace the energy flow path of each utility, in order to understand the actual arrangement of the components depicted in the drawings and specifications.

It is recommended that one tour be devoted to viewing the components on the electrical list and a separate tour to trace the paths of fuel energy. Touring each energy source separately will reinforce the "trunk and branches" image of the path of energy flow and develop the concepts required in the next task, which is to prepare schematic diagrams.

Each tour should begin at the meter and follow the path of energy flow. It is not necessary to actually trace the interconnecting wires, ducts and pipes. The important activity is to visit the point of entry for each energy source, and then to visit each place where that energy is converted, transferred or consumed. In the case of the electrical tour, the energy manager should use a copy of the "electrical riser diagram" as a map of the path to be followed. Starting at the meter, the manager should visit each major electrical distribution panel and read the directory located inside to get an idea of the input sites served by that panel. He or she should carry a schematic floor plan and enter notes on it showing the actual location of the major electrical distribution panels shown on the electrical riser diagram.

The fuels tour should begin at the gas (or other fuel) meter and proceed to the point at which the fuel is converted to steam or hot water in boilers and domestic water heaters. The energy manager should then trace the path to the place where the hot water or steam is finally used in air-handling units to heat and humidify air, to provide cooling in absorptive chillers or to directly heat spaces in perimeter radiation, unit heaters and unit ventilators.

The energy manager should be accompanied on these tours by the building operator, whose knowledge of the systems and the location of components will greatly accelerate the ability to locate and identify the various components.

It is common for novice energy managers to be frustrated by the apparent complexities of the energy-consuming devices and their interconnections. They should not expect to achieve a clear understanding from the first building tour; rather, it is sufficient to begin to visualize the devices and their locations. The concepts of how these devices are combined into systems will gradually become clear as the manager creates schematic diagrams and completes the other tasks described in this book. It is important to be patient and allow the understanding of energy flow to develop gradually.

Figure 3-15. A motor control center is an ideal place to identify large electrical consumers.

## TASK 5: DRAW SCHEMATIC DIAGRAMS

Schematic diagrams provide a method to record the information gathered during the process of listing energy-consuming devices, plan reading, and touring the facility to trace energy paths. The understanding and visualization of systems gained by these efforts can be very difficult to recall later if the information is not recorded in this quickly understood form. This "cartooning" of systems also serves as a discipline to ensure that the systems under consideration are fully understood. Conversely, the inability to complete a schematic diagram indicates that some portions are not yet understood.

It should be stressed that the objective of the schematic diagrams can be met by the most simple drawing. Its first purpose is to provide the energy team members with a quick way to recall their understanding of the relationship of interconnected energy-consuming devices. More complex information can be added to copies of the simple diagram in the future as more is learned about the devices, their methods of control and operating criteria. The original diagram should remain simple, as the first point of reference when a system is to be discussed.

Three basic types of schematic drawings are created in this process:

1. Schematic floor plan drawings, indicating the areas served by each air-handling unit or heat pump.

2. A series of diagrams highlighting the flow of electricity to each major end use (lighting fixtures, receptacles, air handlers and cooling systems). These diagrams are made on copies of the electrical riser diagram.

3. A series of diagrams showing the relationships of energy-consuming devices that are interconnected into systems—heating system, cooling system, electrical distribution and special components such as air-handling units.

The first two groups of schematics consist of information drawn directly on copies of the plan and section drawings collected in Task 1. The third type is cartoon-like drawings of energy-consuming systems within the building.

## Schematic Drawings of Heating/Cooling Zones

The first schematic drawings to create are simply intended to identify the zones for the heating and cooling system. In the case of buildings with central air handlers, it is important to note on the floor plans the area served by each air-handling unit so that future discussions of the appropriate setting and on/off sched-

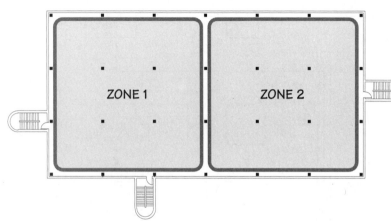

Figure 3-16. Schematic floor plan of an office building showing the area served by each air-handling unit.

ules can proceed from an understanding of the occupants and the areas served. It is recommended that the area served by each air-handling unit be sketched on a copy of the schematic floor plan (see Figure 3-16). A reduction of the actual mechanical floor plans may serve this purpose if they are sufficiently simple and clear.

In the case of buildings with water-to-air heat pumps, the mechanical plan will show the number and location of heat pumps. The general area served by each can be determined by studying the drawing that shows the ductwork leaving each heat pump. A copy of these plans showing heat pumps and the areas they serve should be made for the energy management file (Figure 3-17).

## Schematic Drawings of Electrical Subsystems

Another set of schematic diagrams can be created by drawing on copies of the electrical riser diagram collected as part of an earlier task. It is recommended that this diagram be copied and highlighted to show the flow of electricity to the various electrical end users. Figure 3-18 shows how a copy of the original riser diagram is highlighted to represent the flow of energy to lighting fixtures, for example. This diagram should be entered into the energy management file under the *Lighting* tab of

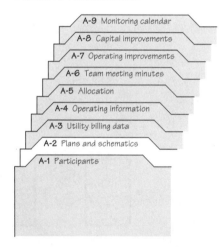

Figure 3-17. Place schematic floor plans of heating/cooling zones into Section A—Tab 2 of the filing system.

Figure 3-18. Electrical riser diagram highlighting overhead lighting panels.

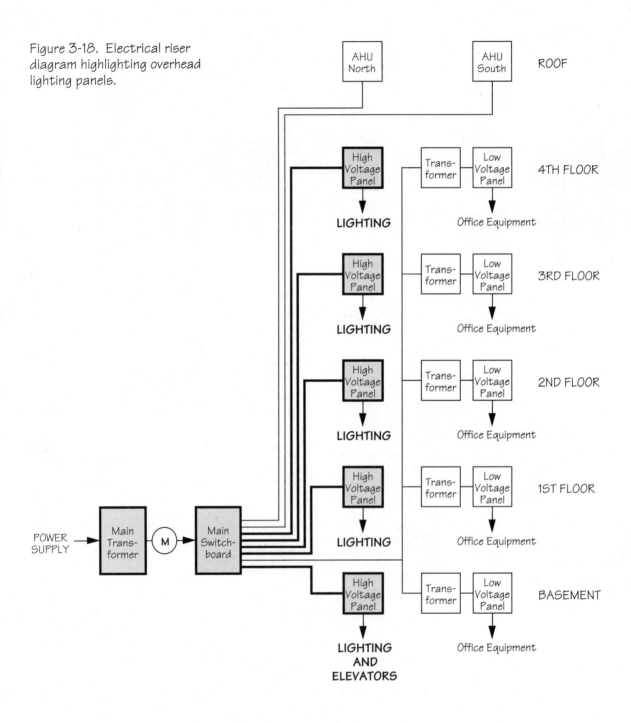

Section B (Figure 3-19). Similar diagrams may be useful to quickly remind the participants of how electricity flows to office equipment, air-handling units, etc., and where measurements could be taken to quantify the electrical use.

## Schematic Drawings of Various Energy-Consuming Devices Interconnected into Systems

The third major group of schematic diagrams consists of simple cartoons that capture the relationships among energy-consuming devices that are interconnected into systems. It is strongly recommended that the start-up process include the creation of these schematic diagrams by the start-up leader with the help of the building operator and with other technical assistance as necessary.

A few basic schematic diagrams are sufficient to begin the energy-efficient operation process. In cold-climate buildings, a schematic diagram showing the path of heating energy as it flows from the fuel meter to the boilers and heaters is recommended (see Figure 3-20). In buildings with central cooling systems a diagram similar to Figure 3-21 is sufficient to document the flow of electrical energy to the cooling system components. In addition to the typical electrical riser diagram (see Figure 3-19), it is sometimes helpful to prepare more detailed diagrams of individual floors or other subdivisions of the total distribution system, similar to the example shown in Figure 3-22.

Along with the general schematic diagrams suggested above, it is sometimes useful to diagram how air-handling units deliver their heating and cooling to the various types of spaces that they serve. Figure 3-23 gives an example of how such a diagram helps the energy management team understand the relationships among heating coils, cooling coils, supply fans, reheat coils and return air systems.

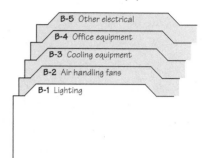

Section B: Electrical equipment

B-5 Other electrical
B-4 Office equipment
B-3 Cooling equipment
B-2 Air handling fans
B-1 Lighting

Figure 3-19. Place schematic versions of electrical riser diagram into the appropriate tabs in Section B of the filing system. If the schematic highlights lighting, for example, then place it in Tab 1—Lighting.

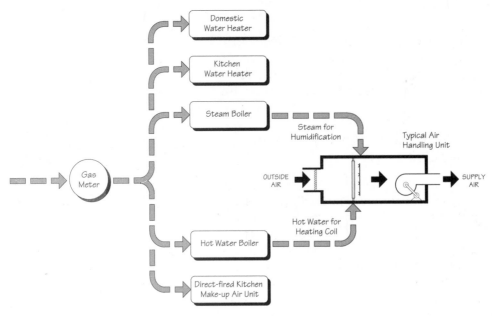

Figure 3-20. Schematic of a heating system.

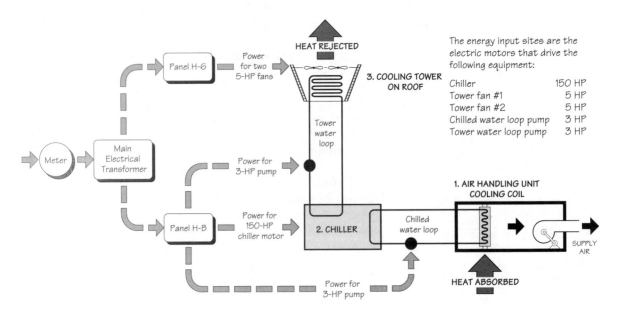

Figure 3-21. Schematic of a typical split chiller system.

Notes: 1. Chilled water in air handling unit cooling coil removes heat from building air.
   2. Chiller transfers heat from the chiller water loop to the tower water loop.
   3. Tower transfers heat to outside air.

## Applying Schematics to Manage Energy

Schematic diagrams are of immeasurable benefit throughout the energy-efficient operation process, as the following actual example illustrates.

An energy management team in a six-story, 252,000-square-foot office building created a diagram of the chiller system, similar to that depicted in Figure 3-21. The process of completing the diagram developed the team's knowledge of energy-consuming devices, their relationships and the relative importance of each. The team studied the diagram and decided that each electrical input site would be measured with electrical dataloggers to determine its actual operating schedule. The datalogging of input sites indicated that all components shut down at 5:00 p.m. as expected, in coincidence with the shutdown of the air-handling unit. However, it was observed that the cooling tower fans came back on shortly after shutdown and ran almost continuously on warm summer nights. The diagram helped to make it clear that the appropriate operating schedule for all components should be determined by the operating schedule of the air-handling units. The team agreed that

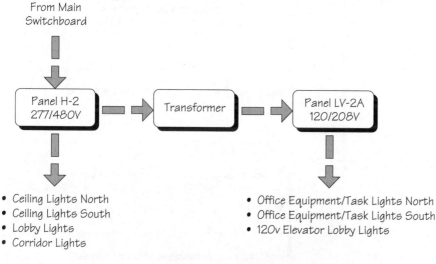

Figure 3-22. Schematic of electrical distribution on a typical floor.

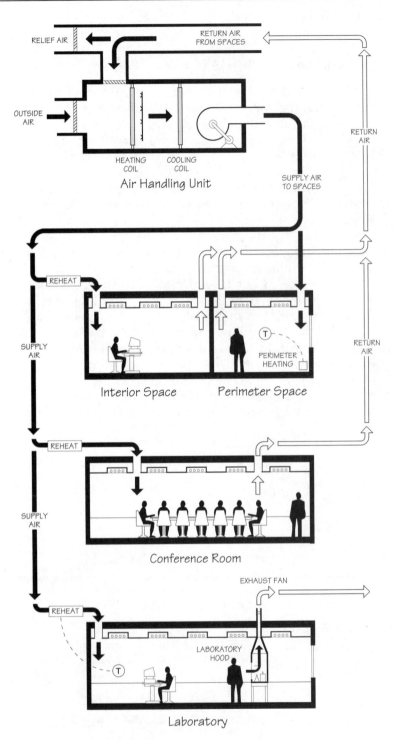

RELIEF AIR

RETURN AIR
FROM SPACES

OUTSIDE
AIR

RETURN
AIR

HEATING
COIL

COOLING
COIL

Air Handling Unit

SUPPLY AIR
TO SPACES

Figure 3-23. Schematic of an air handling unit and the spaces it serves.

REHEAT

SUPPLY
AIR

RETURN
AIR

Interior Space

Perimeter Space

PERIMETER
HEATING

REHEAT

SUPPLY
AIR

Conference Room

EXHAUST FAN

REHEAT

LABORATORY
HOOD

Laboratory

if those units were off and therefore not providing cooling, none of the other components of the system needed to run.

This deviation between the required and actual operating schedule of the tower fans was traced to the temperature sensor in the tower water loop, which was designed to turn on the fans whenever the water loop temperature rose above 85°F. The temperature sensor was located in piping lying directly above the roof, where the hot roof surfaces quickly warmed the water in the pipe after the tower water pump shut off. This rise in water temperature caused the fans to come on and run continuously late into the night, until the roof cooled off sufficiently to allow the water temperature to drop below the sensor setpoint. This malfunction, which apparently had been occurring unnoticed for the entire eight-year life of the building, was quickly remedied by implementing a control strategy, which prevents the tower fans from operating any time the tower water loop pump is off.

Figure 3-24. The improper operation of cooling towers can greatly affect the efficiency of the cooling system.

The above example clearly illustrates how the energy-efficient operation process is facilitated by the clear understanding of systems that schematic diagrams provide.

A primary purpose of schematic diagrams is to record information about energy-consuming systems as this information is gathered and understood. The information can then be quickly recalled when the time comes to apply the energy-efficient operation process to the various energy-consuming systems. Experience has shown that the few basic diagrams suggested above will adequately serve the start-up of the process. As the process matures and as more experience is collected, additional schematics can be prepared to ensure that each new level of information can be recalled when necessary.

# CHAPTER 4

# Estimating Electrical Energy Use

In Chapter 3, the first of the three start-up steps was accomplished by identifying the energy-consuming devices and systems. In this second step (Figure 4-1), a preliminary energy-use estimate is made for each electricity-consuming device in order to understand which ones use the most energy. The purpose of this activity is not to make detailed measurements or to come up with extremely accurate estimates, but rather to make a quick first attempt at allocating where energy is used.

This knowledge of the relative importance of the various energy consumers is critical to keeping the energy-efficient operation process focused on those items whose operating efficiency has the greatest impact. Without this information, energy efficiency teams often spend a disproportionate amount of time improving a small energy user, while neglecting to ensure the efficiency of the equipment that is the most costly to operate.

The four tasks in Step 2 (see Figure 4-2) begin with the collection of electric utility bills so that the actual annual electrical consumption is known. Next, information is gathered on the operating schedule for the electricity-consuming devices and systems that were listed in Step 1. The annual energy use is then estimated for the electrical equipment (Task 3). The last task in this activity is to

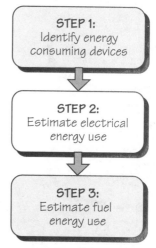

START-UP ACTIVITIES:
Identify and quantify
energy consumers

**STEP 1:**
Identify energy
consuming devices

**STEP 2:**
Estimate electrical
energy use

**STEP 3:**
Estimate fuel
energy use

Figure 4-1. This chapter describes the second step of the energy-efficient operation process.

organize the estimates onto an allocation form similar to Figure 4-10. This establishes a general knowledge of the relative magnitude of these electrical energy consumers.

## TASK 1: ASSEMBLE UTILITY BILL INFORMATION

The energy-efficient operation process requires that certain key information be known about the quantity and pattern of energy input into the building. This information can be obtained from properly organized utility bill data. First, electric utility bill information must be collected and recorded on a spreadsheet. The key information established in this process is (1) the total annual energy input for electricity, (2) the pattern of monthly electrical energy input, and (3) the unit costs of electricity.

### Recording Electric Utility Bill Data

Figure 4-3 illustrates a sample spreadsheet for entering electrical utility bill data. The following steps explain how to collect and record the electric utility bill data:

1. Assemble electrical bills for at least 12 consecutive months and for two or three years if possible.

2. Enter the total monthly kilowatt hours (kWh) from the electric utility bills in Column B of the spreadsheet (Figure 4-3), aligned with the month in which the electricity was consumed (Column A).

   While this may seem simple and obvious, two errors are commonly made at this point. First, building records are often organized and tabulated by accounting personnel who assign them to the month in which the bill was paid. Therefore, if accounting records, rather than the bills, are the source of this information, they may show January's use in February because that is when the bill was received and paid. The second type of

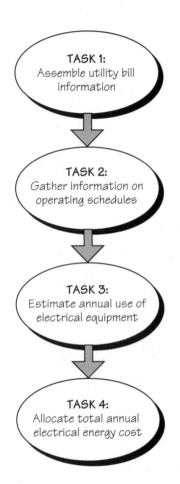

Figure 4-2. Tasks included in Step 2 of the energy-efficient operation process.

Figure 4-3.  Electrical use for example office building.

## 1990 ELECTRICAL USE

| A<br>Month | B<br>Total kWh | C<br>Days | D<br>kWh/Day | E<br>Total Cost | F<br>Unit Cost ($/kWh) | G<br>CDD |
|---|---|---|---|---|---|---|
| JAN | 49,120 | 28 | 1,754 | $2,288.23 | $0.047 | 0 |
| FEB | 53,440 | 30 | 1,781 | $2,370.72 | $0.044 | 0 |
| MAR | 56,320 | 29 | 1,942 | $2,538.66 | $0.045 | 0 |
| APR | 65,120 | 31 | 2,101 | $2,962.27 | $0.045 | 11 |
| MAY | 75,200 | 30 | 2,507 | $3,846.17 | $0.051 | 28 |
| JUN | 105,120 | 34 | 3.092 | $4,868.62 | $0.046 | 178 |
| JUL | 88,430 | 27 | 3,275 | $4,808.55 | $0.054 | 206 |
| AUG | 75,360 | 29 | 2,599 | $4,306.09 | $0.057 | 191 |
| SEP | 68,800 | 29 | 2,372 | $3,379.05 | $0.049 | 125 |
| OCT | 64,800 | 30 | 2,160 | $3,079.28 | $0.048 | 1 |
| NOV | 68,480 | 34 | 2,014 | $3,035.86 | $0.044 | 0 |
| DEC | 57,280 | 33 | 1,736 | $2,610.55 | $0.046 | 0 |
| **TOTALS** | 827,470 | 364 | 2,273 (avg) | $40,094.05 | $0.048 (avg) | 740 |

## 1991 ELECTRICAL USE

| A<br>Month | B<br>Total kWh | C<br>Days | D<br>kWh/Day | E<br>Total Cost | F<br>Unit Cost ($/kWh) | G<br>CDD |
|---|---|---|---|---|---|---|
| JAN | 65,920 | 35 | 1,883 | $2,961.92 | $0.045 | 0 |
| FEB | 48,800 | 24 | 2,033 | $2,563.23 | $0.053 | 0 |
| MAR | 59,680 | 31 | 1,925 | $2,862.99 | $0.048 | 0 |
| APR | 65,280 | 29 | 2,251 | $3,354.95 | $0.051 | 8 |
| MAY | 73,440 | 30 | 2,448 | $4,260.04 | $0.058 | 109 |
| JUN | 99,200 | 33 | 3,006 | $5,219.56 | $0.053 | 246 |
| JUL | 96,160 | 28 | 3.434 | $5,527.53 | $0.057 | 238 |
| AUG | 90,880 | 30 | 3.029 | $5.390.82 | $0.059 | 205 |
| SEP | 77,921 | 29 | 2,687 | $4,060.98 | $0.052 | 51 |
| OCT | 64,000 | 31 | 2.065 | $3,324.28 | $0.052 | 0 |
| NOV | 59,360 | 32 | 1,855 | $2,805.70 | $0.047 | 0 |
| DEC | 57,920 | 33 | 1,755 | $2,748.58 | $0.047 | 0 |
| **TOTALS** | 858,560 | 365 | 2,352 (avg) | $45,080.58 | $0.053 (avg) | 857 |

Figure 4-4. Electric meters show the total quantity of energy used, but provide no information on the profile of energy use over time.

error occurs when the energy use is assigned to the wrong month when the billing periods do not correspond directly to the months. For example, a bill showing energy use from January 11 to February 12 should be assigned to January because the majority of the days in the billing period fell in that month. Both of these potential problems can be avoided by taking information directly from utility bills, and by paying careful attention to the meter reading dates for the start and end of the billing periods.

3. Divide the total kWh entered in Column B by the number of days in the billing period (Column C) and enter the result in Column D. The numbers in Column D represent the average kWh per day used in each month.

This kWh per day number balances out the potentially misleading effect of short and long periods of time between meter readings. For example, if just the monthly total used in the 1990 example were plotted (Column B), July would appear to have less energy use than June only because there are 34 days in the June billing period and only 27 days in the July billing period. A plot of the kWh per day more accurately reflects the rate of energy use in each month.

4. Enter the total billed dollar amount for each month in Column E.

5. Divide the monthly cost entered in Column E by the total kWh (Column B) and enter the result in Column F. The numbers in Column F represent the unit cost of electricity in each month.

An experienced energy manager will recognize that the average cost per kWh arrived at by this method actually represents a blend of commodity costs (kWh) and demand charges. While this is a considerable simplification, it is a reasonable starting point for the novice energy manager to begin the process of estimating the cost of electricity consumed by electrical devices.

6. Enter monthly cooling degree day information (usually available from the nearest national weather reporting station) in Column G.

   Cooling degree days are a general expression of the severity of the weather affecting building cooling loads, with high numbers indicating a higher need for cooling. In buildings with electrically-driven cooling systems, a summertime rise in electrical consumption should be explainable by an increase in cooling degree days. The relationship between a cooling system's electrical consumption and cooling degree days is most analogous during periods when the outdoor temperature is consistently warm (i.e., above 70°). Cooling degree days are not an accurate reflection of cooling load during periods of warm days and cool nights, and the numbers do not account for the effect of humidity on cooling loads. It should also be noted that cooling degree day data are reported in calendar months while electrical bill information usually represents use in portions of two months (e.g., June 10 to July 9). For these reasons, cooling degree days should be used only as a general indicator of cooling energy use and only during consistently warm weather.

7. Total the following columns in the last line of the spreadsheet: Column B (annual kWh used), Column C (days represented), Column E (total cost) and Column G (cooling degree days).

8. Find the average kWh per day by dividing the total of Column B by the total of Column C.

9. Find the average unit cost by dividing the total of Column E by the total of Column B. Enter this average at the bottom of Column F.

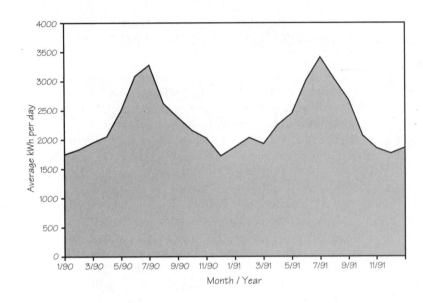

Figure 4-5. Graph indicating the average daily electric use for each month in a two-year period.

## Graphing Electric Utility Bill Data

Plot the kWh per day information from Column D of Figure 4-3 on a graph, as shown in Figure 4-5. These plots can be done manually on graph paper or automatically if the data are entered on a computerized spreadsheet. This plot is useful in showing long-term trends in energy use. For example, Figure 4-5 shows that electrical use was higher in 1991 than in 1990. Further analysis indicates that the use during the winter months was relatively equal for the two-year period and that the increase occurred primarily in the summer months. This may be explained by a warmer summer in 1991 than in 1990. A review of the total annual cooling degree day information from the spreadsheet Column G supports the assumption that the annual difference was due primarily to weather.

The plot in Figure 4-5 is also useful in separating the annual consumption into two major categories—weather-related and non-weather-related electrical use. This process is described in Appendix A. The spreadsheets and graphs for electrical use should be filed in Section A—Tab 3 of the filing system (see Figure 4-6).

**Section A: Administration**

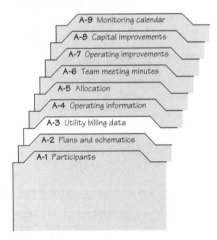

A-9 Monitoring calendar
A-8 Capital improvements
A-7 Operating improvements
A-6 Team meeting minutes
A-5 Allocation
A-4 Operating information
A-3 Utility billing data
A-2 Plans and schematics
A-1 Participants

Figure 4-6. Place electrical use data and graphs in Section A—Tab 3 of the filing system.

## TASK 2: GATHER INFORMATION ON OPERATING SCHEDULES

The purpose of this step in the start-up process is to estimate the annual electrical dollars consumed by each of the electrical energy users identified in Step 1. These estimates are created from information collected on the time of operation for the energy input site.

At this stage it is not important to distinguish between the actual and the required operating schedule. The actual schedule will be measured and the required schedule will be determined later in the process (see Chapter 6). At this point, it is sufficient to approximate actual schedule. This is done by identifying who decides when the equipment goes on and off and asking that person what the expected or estimated operating schedule should be.

The information about operating schedules should be compiled in an operating schedule form. Figure 4-7 shows a suggested form containing information from the example building.

In order to complete the operating schedule form, it is necessary to gather information in a systematic way. Unfortunately, it is difficult to indicate a specific procedure for all buildings because the building systems, people responsible and policies for operation vary widely. In most cases, simple investigation and common sense should lead to the appropriate sources of information. The following activities are useful in collecting this type of information.

1. Interview building occupants to obtain the following information:

   - Standard work schedule when lights and office equipment are typically operated.

   - Schedule and amount of any off-hour use of lights and office equipment (e.g., people who work overtime or on weekends).

Figure 4-7. Operating schedule for energy-consuming equipment.

| Item | Operating schedule | | | | | | hours per week | wks per year | Person responsible | Notes |
|------|--------------------|--|--|--|--|--|------|------|-----|------|
| | Mon-Fri | | Saturday | | Sunday | | | | | |
| | on | off | on | off | on | off | | | | |
| Office overhead lighting<br>10 % on<br>90 % on<br>30 % on | cont.<br>7:00a | 10:00p | cont.<br><br>8:00a | <br><br>2:30p | cont. | | 168<br>75<br>6.5 | 52<br>50<br>50 | Occupants & custodial | |
| Task lighting<br>100 %<br>30 % | 8:00a | 5:00p | <br>8:00a | <br>2:30p | | | 45<br>6.5 | 50<br>50 | | |
| Garage lighting | 6:00a | 10:00p | 8:00a | 4:00p | | | 78 | 52 | Custodial | Operated by a timer |
| Air-handling fans | 4:00a | 5:00p | 6:00a | 3:00p | 10:00a | 2:00p | 78 | 52 | Facility manager | Operates as req'd above 60° outside when air handlers on |
| Office equipment<br>75 % on<br>25 % on | 8:00a<br>cont. | 5:00p | <br>cont. | | <br>cont. | | 45<br>168 | 50<br>52 | | |
| Air conditioning | | | | | | | varies | 30 | Contract maint. | |
| Bathroom exhaust fans | | cont. | | cont. | | cont. | | 168 | 52 maint. | Elec. |
| Elevators | | | | | | | 10 | 50 | | Estimated to operate 25% of time between 8:00a-5:00p on Mon-Fri |

2. Interview custodians to obtain the following information:

   - Schedule and amount of any off-hour use of lights for daily custodial work.

   - The custodians' observations of any off-hour use of lights and office equipment by occupants.

3. Interview building operators to obtain the following information:

   - Operating schedule for any automatically controlled lights.

   - Operating schedule for air-handling units.

   - Enable/disable schedule for boilers and chillers.

For this example building, it was determined that 10 percent of the overhead lighting is on emergency circuits and operates continuously. The remaining 90 percent of the lighting is turned on by the building occupants at approximately 7 a.m. and is turned off by custodians at approximately 10 p.m. on weekdays. The occupants estimated that 30 percent of the non-emergency lighting is used by building occupants between 8 a.m. and 2:30 p.m. on Saturdays. Interviews with building occupants and custodial personnel led to the estimate that 75 percent of the office equipment (computers, printers, copiers, etc.) is switched on at 8 a.m. and off at 5 p.m. by the building occupants, and the remaining 25 percent operates continuously. The air-handling schedule was obtained from the building operator who is responsible for setting the timers that turn the units on and off. The operating schedule information should be filed in Section A—Tab 4 of the filing system (see Figure 4-8).

The process of gathering operating schedule information should continue until all of the listed input sites have been investigated and the persons responsible for the operation of all equipment have been identified. The list of people who influence the operation of energy-consuming equipment will be consulted later in the process, when decisions are made about who should

Section A: Administration

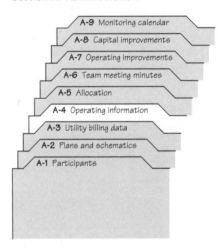

A-9 Monitoring calendar
A-8 Capital improvements
A-7 Operating improvements
A-6 Team meeting minutes
A-5 Allocation
A-4 Operating information
A-3 Utility billing data
A-2 Plans and schematics
A-1 Participants

Figure 4-8. Place operating schedule estimates in Section A—Tab 4 of the filing system.

participate in the energy management team process.

The basic task of gathering operating schedule information often uncovers energy-saving opportunities, as the following example illustrates. While asking how and when lights were turned off, the author received the following responses:

**Building Manager:** "We have an automatic sweep control that turns lights off at 10 p.m.."

**Head Custodian:** "We get done at 8 p.m. We don't turn off lights because that is done automatically after we leave…at about 8:30 p.m., I suppose."

**Head of Night Security:** "The lights go off sometime between our 1 a.m. rounds and our 3 a.m. rounds."

**Control Technician:** "I was asked by custodial to set the control timer to turn lights off at 2 a.m.."

**Head Custodian:** "Yes, I had the timer set for 2 a.m. because we were working late to shampoo carpets. But that was six months ago.… I assumed that the times would be reset when we were done."

As this example illustrates, the process of simply inquiring about operating schedules can uncover energy waste.

## TASK 3: ESTIMATE ANNUAL USE OF ELECTRICAL EQUIPMENT

The objective of this task is to arrive at a rough estimate of the annual energy consumption of each electricity-consuming item listed in Step 1. These estimates provide two significant benefits to the energy-efficient operation process. First, they establish priorities for the energy team by clearly showing which input sites use the most energy and therefore should receive the most attention to ensure operating efficiency. Second, they create a familiarity with the variables that affect the energy use of each input site. To estimate energy use, the energy manager must estimate both rate of consumption and time of use for each significant energy consumer. This activity provides valuable insights into which variables affect each item's energy use and which variables should be monitored to detect inefficient or excess operation.

Appendix A provides detailed descriptions of methods to estimate the annual energy dollars consumed by electrical equipment commonly found in buildings. The purpose of these estimates is to determine the relative magnitude of each energy user and to develop a general familiarity with the variables that affect their energy consumption. A high level of precision is not necessary to accomplish these goals. The estimating methods described were selected so that the intended result can be achieved by people with modest technical capability. Appendix A provides simplified estimating procedures for the electrical devices in an example building, as well as for other typical electrical equipment.

## TASK 4:  ALLOCATE ANNUAL ELECTRICAL ENERGY COSTS

The final task in Start-up Step 2 is to organize the estimated energy use for all the electrical devices so that the relative importance of each can be understood. This is done on an allocation form, such as that illustrated in Figure 4-10. This form provides a simple means of depicting the allocated amounts both numerically and graphically. This graph is extremely valuable because it can quickly convey to everyone involved in the energy management process a balanced overview of the importance of each energy-consuming device in the system.

The following paragraphs describe how all of the tasks related to estimating electrical energy use are brought together to complete an allocation of annual electrical costs to the various electrical consumers:

1. Data from the tabulation of utility bills (Figure 4-3) are entered on the allocation form (Figure 4-10). The most recent year's average unit cost of electricity is entered at Item A, and the total electrical usage and total electrical cost is entered on Line E-12.

Figure 4-9. Many exhaust fans waste energy dollars by operating more hours than necessary.

Figure 4-10. Allocation of annual electrical energy cost.

Item A: $0.053 per kWh (elec. cost)

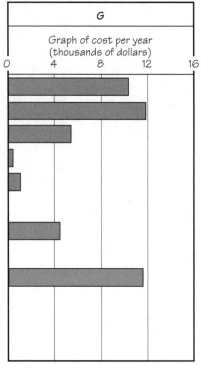

| B | C | D | E | F | G |
|---|---|---|---|---|---|
| ELECTRICAL USE | Item | Estimated annual kWh | Annual cost | Percent of total cost | Graph of cost per year (thousands of dollars) |
| Constant electrical uses | E-1. Lighting | 194,700 | $10,319 | | |
| | E-2. Air handling fans | 225,390 | $11,946 | | |
| | E-3. Office equipment | 102, 345 | $5,424 | | |
| | E-4. Exhaust fans | 9,610 | $509 | | |
| | E-5. Elevators | 20,900 | $1,108 | | |
| | E-6. | | | | |
| | E-7. Miscellaneous | 85,856 | $4,550 | | |
| | E-8. Subtotals | 638,800 | $33,856 | | |
| Weather-variable electrical uses | E-9. Air conditioning | 219,760 | $11,647 | | |
| | E-10. | | | | |
| | E-11. Subtotals | 219,760 | $11,647 | | |
| | E-12. Electric totals | 858,560 | $45,081 | | |

2. The annual kilowatt hours (kWh) used by each electrical consumer is estimated using instructions provided in Appendix A. The estimated use for each is entered in Column D.

3. The estimated annual use of each consumer (Column D) is then multiplied by the average unit cost (Item A) to calculate the estimated annual electrical cost. This value is entered in Column E.

Column F is left blank until estimates of fuel energy users are made (see Chapter 5). The percentages in this column are intended to represent each item's percentage of total energy costs—fuel plus electricity. See Figure 6-2 for an example of Column F completed.

4. Finally, the annual costs for each item in Column E are plotted in the graphic form, as shown under Column G in Figure 4-10. Only the individual consumers of energy—not the subtotals or totals—are plotted. The first step in this process is to determine the appropriate horizontal scale for this graph. The horizontal axis should be scaled to accommodate the largest entry in Column E. In this case, a horizontal scale of $0 to $16,000 was chosen. After the horizontal axis is scaled, a horizontal bar can be drawn for each item, representing the value shown in Column E. These bars can then be shaded to create a thermometer plot that graphically depicts the allocation of energy cost to the building's most significant electrical energy input sites.

The experienced energy manager will recognize that this method distributes electrical demand costs equally among all the items listed in Column C. While a detailed analysis might show that some items represent a disproportionate share of demand costs, this method is sufficiently accurate to achieve the desired general allocation of total annual energy dollars. In most cases, a more detailed analysis would not significantly change either the shape of the graph under Column G or the conclusions that would be drawn from this allocation.

## Completion of the Allocation Process

The next chapter presents a similar process for estimating and allocating the fuel energy use. Once this estimating process has been completed for all energy sources, a combined energy allocation for the building can be created and priorities for energy management established. This total building allocation appears at the beginning of Chapter 6 (see Figure 6-2).

# CHAPTER 5

# Estimating Fuel Energy Use

STEP 1:
Identify energy
consuming devices

STEP 2:
Estimate electrical
energy use

STEP 3:
Estimate fuel
energy use

Figure 5-1. This chapter describes the third step of the energy-efficient operation process.

This start-up activity is similar to the one described in Chapter 4, in which electrical energy use was estimated. This chapter explains how to make a preliminary energy-use estimate for each fuel-consuming device in order to understand which devices use the most energy (see Figure 5-1). The purpose of this activity is not to make detailed measurements or to come up with extremely accurate estimates. Rather, the intention is to devote a limited effort to making a quick first attempt at allocating where fuel is used.

The goal is to understand the relative energy costs of the various fuel consumers, in order to keep the energy-efficient operation process focused on those items whose operating efficiency has the greatest impact. With this information, energy management teams can spend the majority of their time improving the efficiency of the equipment that is the most costly to operate.

A typical example might be an office building where people are attempting to reduce energy consumption by reducing hot water use and are considering investing in more efficient hot water heaters. The focus on water heating may be based on the fact that it is a visible use of energy; or perhaps a water heater salesperson made a convincing presentation with a payback that appears reasonable. This type of well-intentioned activity should proceed only after an overview of the facility's actual energy use is achieved. In this case, for example, the estimating activity may show that hot water use represents only 2 percent of total energy use of the building, while some other category might represent 40 percent. Savings are likely to be much greater if the efforts are first directed toward the large categories of consumption. This overall allocation picture, even if it is a rough estimate, is a critical tool for keeping the energy-efficient operation process cost effective.

The four tasks in this activity (see Figure 5-2) begin with the collection of bills for each utility so that the actual annual fuel consumption is known. Next, information is gathered on the operating schedule for the fuel-consuming devices and systems that were listed in Step 1. The annual energy use is then estimated for each separate fuel-consuming device or system (Task 3). The last task in this activity is organizing the estimates on an allocation form. This establishes a general knowledge of the relative magnitude of these energy consumers.

## TASK 1: ASSEMBLE UTILITY BILL INFORMATION

The energy-efficient operation process requires that certain key information be known about the quantity and pattern of energy input into the building. This information can be obtained from properly organized utility bill data. First, fuel utility bill information must be collected and recorded on a spreadsheet and graphic format. Key information established in this process is (1) the total annual energy input for fuels, (2) the pattern of monthly fuel consumption, and (3) the unit cost of fuel.

### Recording Fuel Utility Bill Data

Energy managers should follow a procedure similar to that used for electrical utility data (Chapter 4) to record fuel bill information. In most cases, the explanations given in the previous chapter for the electrical spreadsheet are applicable to the fuels spreadsheet shown in Figure 5-3. This spreadsheet is based on an example building using natural gas, but a similar procedure would be used for any fuel type. Energy managers

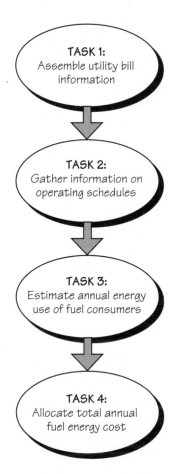

**TASK 1:**
Assemble utility bill information

**TASK 2:**
Gather information on operating schedules

**TASK 3:**
Estimate annual energy use of fuel consumers

**TASK 4:**
Allocate total annual fuel energy cost

Figure 5-2. Tasks included in Step 3 of the energy-efficient operation procedure.

Figure 5-3. Natural gas use for example office building.

## 1990 NATURAL GAS USE

| A Month | B Total CCF | C Days | D CCF/Day | E Total | F Unit Cost ($/CCF) | G HDD |
|---------|-------------|--------|-----------|---------|---------------------|-------|
| JAN | 5,987 | 32 | 187 | $2,650.63 | $0.443 | 1194 |
| FEB | 4,123 | 31 | 133 | $1,818.59 | $0.441 | 1151 |
| MAR | 3,670 | 30 | 122 | $1,617.78 | $0.441 | 899 |
| APR | 2,955 | 31 | 95 | $1,292.25 | $0.437 | 569 |
| MAY | 1,832 | 27 | 68 | $786.21 | $0.429 | 274 |
| JUN | 230 | 32 | 7 | $98.90 | $0.430 | 37 |
| JUL | 251 | 30 | 8 | $107.43 | $0.428 | 2 |
| AUG | 245 | 32 | 8 | $105.84 | $0.432 | 5 |
| SEP | 402 | 30 | 13 | $176.88 | $0.440 | 136 |
| OCT | 2,220 | 29 | 77 | $936.05 | $0.422 | 516 |
| NOV | 3,625 | 29 | 125 | $1,557.25 | $0.430 | 820 |
| DEC | 6,259 | 33 | 190 | $2,688.46 | $0.430 | 1484 |
| TOTALS | 31,799 | 366 | 87 (avg) | $13,836.27 | $0.435 (avg) | 7087 |

## 1991 NATURAL GAS USE

| A Month | B Total CCF | C Days | D CCF/Day | E Total | F Unit Cost ($/CCF) | G HDD |
|---------|-------------|--------|-----------|---------|---------------------|-------|
| JAN | 7,998 | 34 | 235 | $3,582.84 | $0.448 | 1624 |
| FEB | 5,511 | 28 | 197 | $2,529.05 | $0.459 | 1130 |
| MAR | 5,092 | 29 | 176 | $2,314.45 | $0.455 | 945 |
| APR | 3,534 | 31 | 114 | $1,523.77 | $0.431 | 481 |
| MAY | 1,082 | 30 | 36 | $460.92 | $0.426 | 197 |
| JUN | 250 | 31 | 8 | $106 .25 | $0.425 | 481 |
| JUL | 270 | 33 | 8 | $116.37 | $0.431 | 7 |
| AUG | 200 | 29 | 7 | $87.63 | $0.438 | 8 |
| SEP | 516 | 30 | 17 | $230.69 | $0.447 | 228 |
| OCT | 2,331 | 31 | 75 | $1,061.17 | $0.455 | 548 |
| NOV | 3,236 | 29 | 112 | $1,473.51 | $0.455 | 1206 |
| DEC | 5,463 | 31 | 176 | $2,547.72 | $0.466 | 1354 |
| TOTALS | 35,483 | 366 | 97 (avg) | $16,038.37 | $0.452 (avg) | 7731 |

should follow these steps to collect and record the fuel utility bill data:

1. Assemble fuel bills for at least 12 consecutive months and for two or three years if possible.

2. Enter the total monthly usage from the utility bills in Column B of the spreadsheet (Figure 5-3) aligned with the month in which the energy was consumed (Column A). The units of energy shown on this gas use spreadsheet are in hundreds of cubic feet (ccf). Large gas users may find it more convenient to express gas use in thousands of cubic feet (mcf).

3. Divide the total ccf you entered in Column B by the number of days in the billing period (Column C) and enter the result in Column D. The numbers in Column D represent the average ccf per day used in each month.

4. Enter the total billed dollar amount for each month in Column E.

5. Divide the monthly cost you entered in Column E by the total ccf (Column B) to calculate the unit cost. The unit cost from this calculation will be expressed in dollars per ccf. Place the answer in Column F. The numbers in Column F represent the unit cost of fuel energy for each month.

6. Enter monthly heating degree day information (usually available from the nearest national weather reporting station) in Column G. Heating degree days are a general expression of the severity of the weather affecting building heating loads, with high numbers indicating a higher need for heating. Heating degree days are most applicable in periods of consistently cold weather.

7. On the bottom line of the spreadsheet, total Column B (annual ccf used), Column C (days represented), Column E (total cost) and Column G (heating degree days).

8. Find the average of Column D (ccf per day) and Column F (unit cost) and record this number on the bottom line of the fuel allocation form (Figure 5-7). These total annual fuel units (ccf) and fuel dollars will be allocated to the fuel consumer shown in Column B of the allocation form.

## Working with Two or More Fuel Types

The fuel spreadsheet in the above example is based on a building using only natural gas. Some facilities have interruptible gas service that occasionally requires using oil or propane as a back-up fuel source. In such cases, use the following procedure to create a combined fuel use spreadsheet, like the one shown in Figure 5-4.

1. Enter information from gas bills in Columns B, C and E.

2. Convert gas units from cubic feet to millions of Btu (MMBtu) and enter this number in Column D.

$$MMBtu = ccf \text{ of gas}/10$$

$$MMBtu = mcf \text{ of gas}$$

3. Estimate gallons of back-up fuel burned in each month and enter this number in Column F.

4. Convert units from gallons to millions of Btu (MMBtu) using the following formulas and enter the number in Column G.

$$MMBtu = gallons \text{ of } \#2 \text{ oil} \times 0.14$$

$$MMBtu = gallons \text{ of } \#6 \text{ oil} \times 0.15$$

$$MMBtu = gallons \text{ of propane} \times 0.092$$

5. Enter the cost per gallon paid for oil or propane in Column H, and calculate each month's cost by multiplying Column F by Column H. Enter the cost in Column J.

6. Calculate the total MMBtu of fuel used in each month by adding Column D to Column G. Enter the total in Column K.

7. Calculate the total cost for each month by adding Column E to Column J. Enter the total cost in Column L.

8. Calculate the average cost per MMBtu by dividing Column L by Column K and enter it in Column M.

9. Calculate MMBtu per day by dividing Column K by Column B and enter the number in Column N.

10. At the bottom of the spreadsheet, total Columns B (days represented), K (total MMBtu), L (total dollars) and O (total heating degree days).

11. Divide the total of Column L by the total of Column K to determine the average unit cost, and enter it at the bottom of Column M.

The totals from this combined fuel use spreadsheet can now be entered at the bottom of the allocation form and used to plot the annual fuel use consumption profile.

Figure 5-4. Spreadsheet illustrating combined natural gas and other fuel use.

| A | B | C | D | E | F | G | H | J | K | L | M | N | O |
|---|---|---|---|---|---|---|---|---|---|---|---|---|---|
| | | | Gas | | | #2 Fuel Oil | | | | | | | |
| Mon | Days | CCF | MMBtu | Gas cost | Gallon | MMBtu | Cost per gallon | Oil cost | Total MMBtu | Total cost | Cost per MMBtu | MMBtu per day | HDD |
| JAN | 33 | 5,140 | 514.0 | $2,271 | 915 | 128.0 | $0.78 | $713 | 642 | $2,984 | $4.65 | 19.4 | 1306 |
| FEB | 29 | 4,675 | 467.5 | $1,986 | 835 | 117.0 | $0.78 | $651 | 584 | $2,638 | $4.51 | 20.1 | 1182 |
| MAR | 29 | 3,303 | 330.3 | $1,417 | 260 | 36.7 | $0.78 | $204 | 367 | $1,621 | $4.42 | 12.6 | 902 |
| APR | 31 | 2,955 | 295.5 | $1,292 | | | | | 296 | $1,292 | $4.37 | 9.5 | 569 |
| MAY | 30 | 1,832 | 183.2 | $786 | | | | | 183 | $786 | $4.29 | 6.8 | 274 |
| JUN | 31 | 230 | 23.0 | $99 | | | | | 23 | $99 | $4.30 | 0.7 | 37 |
| JUL | 33 | 251 | 25.1 | $107 | | | | | 25 | $107 | $4.28 | 0.8 | 2 |
| AUG | 29 | 245 | 24.5 | $106 | | | | | 25 | $106 | $4.32 | 0.8 | 5 |
| SEP | 30 | 402 | 40.2 | $177 | | | | | 40 | $177 | $4.40 | 1.3 | 136 |
| OCT | 31 | 2,220 | 222.0 | $936 | | | | | 220 | $936 | $4.42 | 7.7 | 516 |
| NOV | 28 | 3,094 | 309.4 | $1,330 | 390 | 54.6 | $0.84 | $328 | 364 | $1,658 | $4.55 | 13.0 | 820 |
| DEC | 31 | 4,382 | 438.2 | $1,884 | 1340 | 187.8 | $0.84 | $1,127 | 626 | $3,011 | $4.81 | 20.2 | 1384 |
| TOT | 365 | | | | | | | | 3395 | $15,415 | $4.54 (average) | | 7187 |

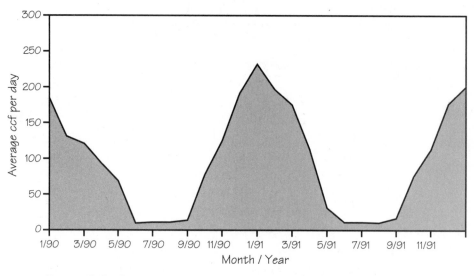

Figure 5-5. Graph indicating the average daily fuel use for each month of the year based on spreadsheet data (Figure 5-3).

Section A: Administration

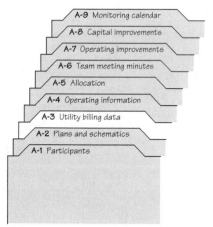

Figure 5-6. Place fuel use data and graphs in Section A—Tab 3 of the filing system.

## Graphing Fuel Utility Bill Data

Plot the fuel ccf per day information from Column D of Figure 5-3 (or the fuel MMBtu per day from Column N of Figure 5-4) on a graph, as shown in Figure 5-5. This can be done manually on graph paper or automatically if the data are entered on a computerized spreadsheet. Similar to the graph done for electrical use, this plot is useful in showing long-term trends in fuel energy use.

The plot in Figure 5-5 is also useful in separating the annual consumption into two major categories—weather-variable and constant fuel use. This process is described in Appendix B. The spreadsheets and graphs for natural gas use should be filed in Section A—Tab 3 of the filing system (see Figure 5-6).

# TASK 2: GATHER INFORMATION ON OPERATING SCHEDULES

Later steps in the energy-efficient operation process call for developing energy use profiles for each major energy input site. These profiles, similar to Figure 5-5, show the rate of energy use plotted over the time of energy use. In order to create these profiles, it is necessary to gather information on the time of operation for the energy input site.

At this stage, it is not important to distinguish between the actual and the required operating schedule. The actual schedule will be measured and the required schedule will be determined in the process described in Chapter 6. At this point, it is sufficient to determine an approximation of the actual schedule. This is done by identifying who decides when the equipment goes on and off and asking that person what the expected or estimated operating schedule should be. Based on the list of devices compiled in Chapter 3, an operating schedule form such as that shown in Figure 5-7 should be created to record this information.

In order to complete the operating schedule form, it is necessary to gather information in a systematic way. Unfortunately, it is difficult to recommend a specific procedure for all buildings since the building systems, people responsible and policies for operation vary

Figure 5-7. Operating schedule for energy consuming equipment.

| | Operating schedule | | | | | | | | wks | |
|---|---|---|---|---|---|---|---|---|---|---|
| | Mon-Fri | | Saturday | | Sunday | | per | hours per | Person | |
| Item | on | off | on | off | on | off | week | year | responsible | Notes |
| Heating boiler | | | | | | | varies | 28 | Contract maintenance | Enabled Oct. 15-May 15 |
| Water heaters | | | | | | | varies | 52 | Mechanical maintenance | Operates as required to meet needs of toilet rooms and kitchen |

**Section A: Administration**

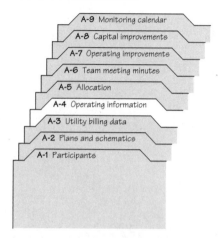

A-9 Monitoring calendar
A-8 Capital improvements
A-7 Operating improvements
A-6 Team meeting minutes
A-5 Allocation
A-4 Operating information
A-3 Utility billing data
A-2 Plans and schematics
A-1 Participants

Figure 5-8. Place operating schedule estimates in Section A—Tab 4 of the filing system.

widely. In a typical circumstance, simple investigation and common sense should lead to the appropriate sources of information. For fuel use, typical information to be collected includes the operating schedule for air-handling units and the enable/disable schedule for boilers and chillers.

In the example building, the air-handling schedule was obtained from the building operator who is responsible for setting the timers that turn the units on and off. The contract maintenance person responsible for boiler operation reported that the boiler is enabled between October 15 and May 15 and that the actual hours of operation are determined by weather conditions. The water heaters are enabled continuously, and their actual operation is determined by toilet room hot water use. The information for the example building is entered on the form in Figure 5-7. The operating schedule information should be filed in Section A—Tab 4 of the filing system (see Figure 5-8).

The process of gathering operating schedule information should continue until all of the listed input sites

Figure 5-9. Space heating boilers are large energy consumers in cold climates.

have been investigated and the people responsible for the operation of all equipment have been identified. The list of individuals who influence the operation of energy-consuming equipment will be consulted later in the process, when decisions are made about who should participate in the energy management team process.

## TASK 3: ESTIMATING ANNUAL ENERGY COST OF FUEL-CONSUMING EQUIPMENT

This task involves estimating the annual cost of fuel used by each significant fuel-consuming device. This information is necessary to determine which are the most costly—and, therefore, the most important—devices to operate efficiently.

Appendix B provides instruction for estimating the fuel used by devices commonly found in buildings. The methods are simple enough to be used by people with modest technical capability, but are sufficiently accurate to accomplish the intended purpose.

## TASK 4: ALLOCATE TOTAL ANNUAL FUEL ENERGY COSTS

The final task in Start-up Step 3 is to organize the estimated fuel use for all the input sites so that the relative importance of each fuel-consuming device or system can be understood. This is done on the allocation summary form depicted in Figure 5-11. The allocation is based on the most recent year's metered fuel use and cost, ensuring that the total allocation represents actual building performance. It converts fuel consumption into dollars so that the annual cost of all energy sources can be compared. Finally, this method provides a simple means of depicting the allocated amount graphically. This graph is immensely valuable because it quickly conveys to everyone involved in the energy-efficient operation process a balanced overview of the importance of each energy-consuming device or system.

Figure 5-10. Annual metered natural gas use should be allocated to various gas consumers.

Figure 5-11. Allocation of annual fuel energy cost.

| Item A: $0.452 per ccf (fuel cost) |
|---|

| B | C | D | E | F | G |
|---|---|---|---|---|---|
| | Item | Estimated annual ccf | Annual cost | Percent of total cost | Graph of cost per year (thousands of dollars) 0  4  8  12  16 |
| Constant natural gas uses | F-1. Domestic hot water | 1,214 | $549 | | |
| | F-2. | | | | |
| | F-3. Subtotals: | 1,214 | $549 | | |
| Weather-variable natural gas uses | F-4. Space heating | 34,269 | $15,489 | | |
| | F-5. | | | | |
| | F-6. Subtotals: | 34,269 | $15,489 | | |
| | F-7. Natural gas totals | 35,483 | $16,038 | | |

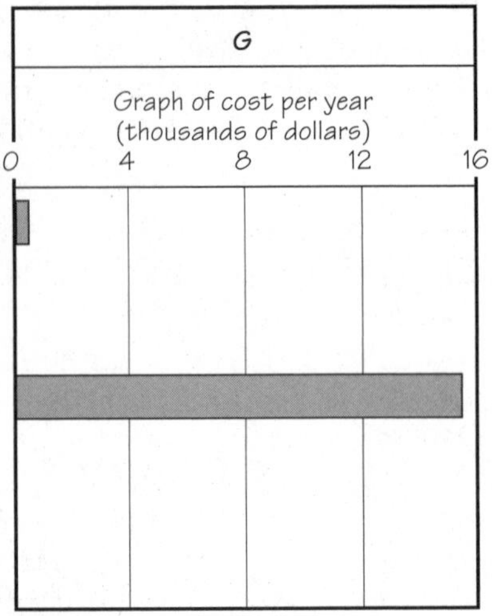

The following steps review the previous tasks in this chapter and describe how to complete the allocation form in Figure 5-11.

1. Data from the tabulation of fuel bills (Figure 5-3 or 5-4) are entered on the allocation form shown in Figure 5-11. The most recent year's average unit cost of fuels is entered at item "A fuels," and the total fuels consumption and cost are entered on Line F-7.

2. The annual fuel use for each consumer is estimated using the instructions provided in Appendix B. The estimated use for each is entered in Column D.

3. The estimated annual use of each consumer (Column D) is then multiplied by the average unit cost (Item A fuels) to calculate the estimated annual fuel cost. This value is entered in Column E. (Column F is left blank until the electrical allocation is combined with the fuels allocation, as explained in Chapter 6.)

4. Finally, the annual costs for each item in Column E are plotted in the graphic form shown under Column G in Figure 5-11. Only the individual components of energy use—not the subtotals or totals—should be plotted. The first step in this process is to determine the appropriate horizontal scale for this graph. The horizontal axis should be scaled to accommodate the largest entry in Column E. In this case, a horizontal scale of $0 to $16,000 was chosen. After the horizontal axis is scaled, a horizontal bar can be drawn for each item, representing the value shown in Column E. These bars can then be shaded to create a thermometer plot that graphically depicts the allocation of energy cost to the building's most significant fuel consumers.

## Completion of the Allocation Process

In the previous chapter, a similar process was presented to estimate and allocate electrical energy costs. Once this process has been completed for all energy sources, combined energy allocations for the building can be created and priorities for energy management established. This total building allocation appears at the beginning of Chapter 6.

# A Process for Achieving Operating Efficiency

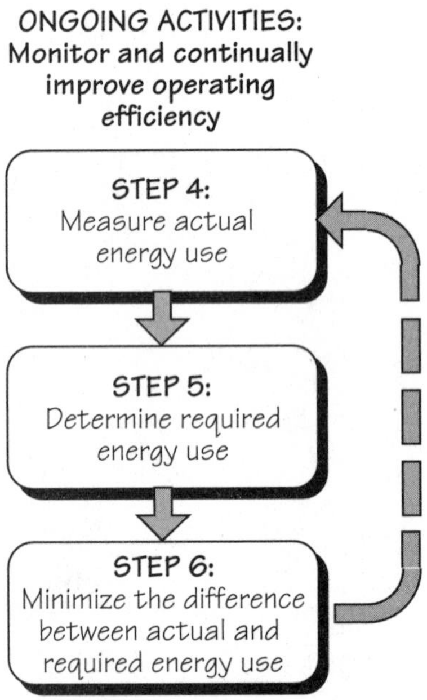

ONGOING ACTIVITIES:
**Monitor and continually improve operating efficiency**

**STEP 4:**
Measure actual energy use

**STEP 5:**
Determine required energy use

**STEP 6:**
Minimize the difference between actual and required energy use

Figure 6-1. This chapter describes the last three ongoing steps in the energy-efficient operation process.

The previous three chapters described the start-up activities required before beginning the ongoing energy-efficient operation process. This chapter describes the three steps of the ongoing process. Figure 6-1 shows these last three steps: Step 4—measure actual energy use; Step 5—determine required energy use; and Step 6—minimize the difference between actual and required energy use. Before these three steps are explained, some key preparation tasks are reviewed. In Chapters 7 and 8, the three-step process is applied to the operation of lighting systems and air-handling units.

## PREPARATION

### Deciding Where to Begin

Chapters 4 and 5 were devoted to estimating the annual cost of energy used by electricity-consuming devices and fuel-consuming devices. These two categories of energy users are summarized at the end of each chapter and can be combined into one table, as shown in Figure 6-2. This allocation of the total annual energy dollars to the various energy-consuming devices and systems provides the energy manager with the necessary perspective to establish a cost-effective process that focuses on the largest energy users.

## Figure 6-2. Allocation of annual energy cost.

### ELECTRICAL USE

Item A: $0.053 per kWh (elec. cost)

| B | C | D | E | F | G |
|---|---|---|---|---|---|
| | Item | Estimated annual kWh | Annual cost | Percent of total cost | Graph of cost per year (thousands of dollars)  0   4   8   12   16 |
| Constant electrical uses | E-1. Lighting | 194,700 | $10,319 | 17 % | |
| | E-2. Air handling fans | 225,390 | $11,946 | 19 % | |
| | E-3. Office equipment | 102,345 | $5,424 | 9 % | |
| | E-4. Exhaust fans | 9,610 | $509 | 1 % | |
| | E-5. Elevators | 20,900 | $1,108 | 2 % | |
| | E-6. | | | | |
| | E-7. Miscellaneous | 85,856 | $4,550 | 7 % | |
| | E-8. Subtotals | 638,800 | $33,856 | 55 % | |
| Weather-variable electrical uses | E-9. Air conditioning | 219,760 | $11,647 | 19 % | |
| | E-10. | | | | |
| | E-11. Subtotals | 219,760 | $11,647 | 19 % | |
| | E-12. Electric totals | 858,560 | $45,081 | 74 % | |

### FUEL USE

Item A: $0.452 per ccf (fuel cost)

| B | C | D | E | F | G |
|---|---|---|---|---|---|
| FUEL USE (Natural gas) | Item | Estimated annual ccf | Annual cost | Percent of total cost | Graph of cost per year (thousands of dollars)  0   4   8   12   16 |
| Constant natural gas uses | F-1. Domestic hot water | 1,214 | $549 | 1 % | |
| | F-2. | | | | |
| | F-3. Subtotals: | 1,214 | $549 | 1 % | |
| Weather-variable natural gas uses | F-4. Space heating | 34,269 | $15,489 | 25 % | |
| | F-5. | | | | |
| | F-6. Subtotals: | 34,269 | $15,489 | 25 % | |
| | F-7. Natural gas totals | 35,483 | $16,038 | 26 % | |

| GRAND TOTAL | All energy totals: | | $61,119 | 100 % |
|---|---|---|---|---|

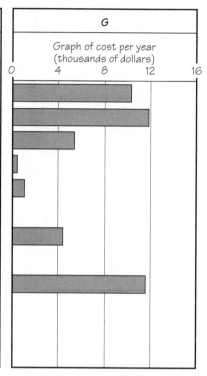

Figure 6-2 should be used to establish the order in which the various energy consumers will be carried through the energy-efficient operation process described in this chapter. As a general rule, the energy manager should start with the equipment that consumes the most energy dollars and proceed progressively toward the least costly equipment. As the manager gains experience, it will become clear at what point the amount of energy is so small and/or the potential cost savings so insignificant that the particular device or system does not warrant the attention of this complete efficient operation process.

One other factor should be considered when deciding where to start this process. As Chapters 7 and 8 illustrate, achieving operating efficiency is a team process involving everyone who influences the operation of energy-consuming devices. It is important for the novice energy management team to choose a first topic that is relatively simple technically so that all participants can understand the issues and successfully participate in each step of the process. It is recommended that the novice team start by analyzing overhead lighting. Because this technology is understood by everyone, it provides an instructive first experience in the key elements of this process.

## Collect and Organize Information

As explained in Chapter 3, it is recommended that a file be created for each item as a place to store and quickly retrieve all information collected. These files not only will enhance the results of the initial analysis, but also will streamline any future repetition of the process.

Specific information about the device or devices to be managed should be gathered and placed in the energy management file. This should include general information on the item's location, size, capacity for energy consumption, operating settings and expected schedule of operation. For example, information on a boiler or hot water heater may include its rated energy input and output, its outlet water set point and its enable/disable operation. For a lighting panel, the information may include a plan showing the location of the panel, a plan showing the location of the lighting served by that panel, the type and quantity of lighting fixtures, their typical wattage and their expected operating schedules.

One of the most important and useful pieces of information to have at hand during the management process is a general understanding of how the device or system is controlled. The method of control typically is the most influential factor determining the best possible operation of a device. For example, the best possible operation of overhead lighting in an office area with multiple switching may be a pattern that reflects the occupancy of the various switched zones. However, the best possible operation of overhead lighting with a single switch in a similar office area would consist of all lighting going on when the first person arrives and going off as the last person leaves.

## Determine Who Should Participate

In order to achieve and sustain energy-efficient building operation, it is essential to secure the participation and cooperation of everyone who influences how and when a device operates.

The importance of this participation cannot be overemphasized. Most energy conservation programs fail to achieve operating efficiency because the energy management team, typically composed of facilities and maintenance personnel, soon recognizes that the operation of most devices is influenced by persons over whom they have no control. The team despairs of achieving operating efficiency and instead devotes its attention to the purchase and installation of more efficient equipment. Unfortunately, this new equipment is often operated inefficiently because no process has been established to identify all of the influencers and involve them in an operating efficiency program.

### Establish a Specific Goal

The energy-efficient process will be better focused if its general goal is made specific for each item to be managed. *The general goal, in its simplest terms, is to ensure that energy-consuming devices use only as much energy as is necessary to do the job they are intended to do.* This goal could be made specific to a lighting panel, for example, by stating that the objective is to ensure that the lighting supplied by this panel operates only when the spaces served by the lighting are occupied.

Referring to this specific goal each time the energy management team meets to discuss this item will help keep the team focus on achieving operating efficiency and avoid becoming sidetracked by the common tendency to intermingle discussions about equipment replacement with discussions of operating efficiency.

## STEP 4: MEASURE ACTUAL ENERGY USE

Measuring the actual performance of energy consuming equipment is perhaps the single most important component of the process described in this book. A fundamental skill necessary to managing anything, whether it be the output of labor, the productivity of a process or the energy-efficient operation of equipment, is the ability to periodically and routinely measure performance. Until recently there has been relatively little true performance measurement in the field of energy efficiency, partly because of the lack of affordable, easy to use measuring tools; and partly because of the apparent complexity of the task of measuring and verifying the operation of all the sensors, controls and devices that must perform correctly to ensure efficient operation. The following paragraphs discuss the recent advances in measurements tools that have made them affordable and easy to use, and describe an approach that greatly simplifies the measurement process.

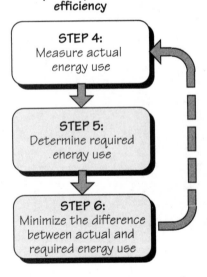

Figure 6-3. Measuring actual use is the first step in the ongoing energy-efficient operation process.

## Measuring Rate Over Time

The quantity of energy consumed by any device is determined by the rate at which it uses energy and by the time over which it operates. Some devices consume energy at a fixed rate, but their time of operation can vary (e.g., a light fixture); some consume energy at a variable rate but may operate continuously (e.g., variable-speed pump); and many devices are variable in both rate and time of energy use (e.g., heat pumps, variable-speed air handlers). Therefore, measurements of energy performance must provide information on both rate of energy use and time of operation.

The most common approach to measuring energy consumption is to use data from utility meters, which typically represent the accumulated units of energy used in a one month billing period. However, this information is of little use to the process described in this book for several reasons. First, utility meters report the aggregated energy use of all energy consumers and therefore provide little or no information on the performance of individual pieces of equipment. Second, meter data depict the results of rate of use over time of operation as a single number—the units of energy used in the meter-reading interval. This number offers no information about how much energy was used at what times.

Because the energy manager's goal is to ensure that each significant energy consumer uses no more than the required amount of energy at each moment in time, measuring tools that both provide rate and time information must be used.

## Tools for Measuring Energy Performance

The energy management process described in this text is based on the ability to actually measure energy use and/or the key variables that indicate energy use during the time at which that use is occurring (i.e., to record actual performance profiles). To implement this process, the energy manager must acquire tools that collect measurements over time, commonly referred to as dataloggers.

*Pen Chart Recorders*

One type of datalogger is the pen chart recorder, which continuously records readings of variables such as temperature, humidity and electrical current in the form of a line drawn on a circle chart or on a continuous paper strip chart. Another family of dataloggers consists of devices that take readings at pre-set intervals (typically 15, 30 or 60 minutes) and print these measurements on paper in the form of columns of numbers. Pen chart recorders essentially provide a continuous profile of energy use over time, and the devices that read at intervals can offer an acceptable simulation of a continuous profile if the reading intervals are sufficiently short.

However, these devices have a number of limitations. They are often quite expensive, are frequently too large to be used unobtrusively, usually require an electrical outlet to supply power and are difficult to install and remove from the measuring location. Perhaps the most serious limitation is the difficulty they present in analyzing the data they collect. Analyzing the performance of an energy-consuming device usually requires simultaneous comparison of several lines of information (e.g., outside air temperature, supply air temperature and space temperature). When this information is contained in several charts or columns of numbers, the energy manager usually must transpose all the data onto hand-drawn profiles in order to perform the necessary analysis.

*Trend-Logging with Building Control Systems*

Recent advances in electronic datalogging have revolutionized the energy management process by placing the key skill of measuring energy use profiles within the grasp of all energy managers. These devices address most of the limitations of their predecessors and have additional features that greatly facilitate the operations management process. Most electronic building control systems sold today have the capability to trend some of the points sensed and equipment controlled. An added advantage of trend-logging systems is that their permanently installed sensing points eliminate the need to install and remove instruments. The larger and more sophisticated systems can trend-log all of their points by recording readings at user-selected intervals, storing these readings and later presenting the data in the form of charts or graphs. While these trend-logging systems vary widely in the number of the points sensed, form of data output and ease of use, they all offer the essential capability to profile performance over time.

Trend-logging with the building control system has two limitations. First, its accuracy depends on the accuracy of the sensors being recorded. Much undetected energy waste is due to inaccurate data in the control system, so trend-logging these points without first verifying their accuracy would fail to detect an energy-wasting malfunction. The second limitation is that many points of measurement that are useful to the energy manager do not represent significant control data and therefore cannot justify permanently installed sensing devices. Examples include sensors that read electrical use by lighting, office equipment and motors, and sensors that read air temperatures at reheat coils and heat pumps.

A number of portable dataloggers are available (and more will undoubtedly appear in the future) that can supplement building control system trend-logging and collect all the necessary data in facilities that have no permanently installed datalogging capability. The following paragraphs describe the key characteristics of these portable dataloggers and the features that are most important to the energy manager.

*Portable Electronic Dataloggers*

Portable electronic dataloggers are battery powered and therefore can be installed in the sensing location without concern for the availability of auxiliary power. Because they are small (some are smaller than a package of cigarettes), they can be easily and quickly placed directly in the area where readings are required (e.g., duct work, air handlers, return air plenums, electrical cabinets). Electronic dataloggers come in compatible families of instruments that allow temperature, humidity, electrical current, pressure, etc., to be measured with a group of instruments that all are operated by the same user-friendly software. These dataloggers collect and store readings at intervals that can be selected by the energy manager; some have the capacity to store more than 30,000 readings.

Perhaps the most important benefit of electronic dataloggers is that they enhance the process of data analysis and data storage. When the dataloggers are returned from the field and attached to a personal computer via its serial port, the readings are downloaded into software that stores the readings in files that can later be called up on the screen and analyzed in the form of a line graph. These graphic profiles of measurements are dramatically easier to analyze than similar information in the form of a strip chart, a circle

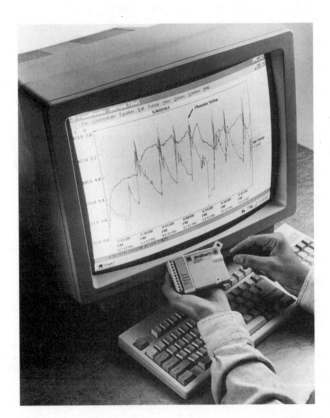

Figure 6-4. Portable electronic dataloggers have revolutionized the process of measuring actual energy use.

chart or columns of numbers. Datalogger software also has the significant advantage of allowing numerous lines of data to be drawn on the same graph, greatly facilitating the process of analyzing multiple variables. Some software also makes it possible to enlarge portions of graphs for more detailed analysis and will perform statistical functions on the lines of data. Finally, the progression towards extremely user-friendly software and reductions in price have placed the ability to record the performance profile of energy-consuming devices within reach of all energy managers.

The measurement procedures described in this book are based on the use of portable electronic dataloggers. Energy managers committed to these procedures must acquire some capability to perform the necessary rate-over-time measurements that they entail.

## What to Measure

One significant inhibitor to achieving energy-efficient operation is the perception that the appropriate operation of energy-consuming devices can be verified only by checking the operation of all the variables that influence their operation. For example, some measurement specialists hold that the only way to determine whether or not an air handler is operating properly is to check every setpoint, calibrate every sensor, check each damper motor and valve, check all pneumatic or electronic control signals and review the control logic or electronic control software programs. While some or all of these checks may at some time be necessary to diagnose the exact cause of a malfunction, only a few are necessary to detect whether an energy-wasting malfunction exists at all.

This distinction between detecting a malfunction and diagnosing its cause is critical to making the energy-efficient operation process cost effective and sustainable over the long term. One of the essential features of the process described in this book is the identification of those few *key operating variables* that, if periodically measured, will allow the energy management team to determine whether a device or system is operating efficiently or whether an energy-wasting malfunction is present. Only when a malfunction is detected are more extensive investigations made to diagnose and eliminate its cause. The following example illustrates this process.

An air handler or rooftop unit is programmed to operate during specified occupied hours but can also run during unoccupied hours if space temperatures reach certain extremes of heat or cold. It can also start early if necessary to achieve desired conditions for morning occupancy. The process of simply determining whether or not the unit's on/off schedule is appropriate normally entails checking or verifying all of the following components:

- On/off software program or timer setting.

- Function of timer.

- Accuracy of timer reference clock time.

- Calibration of override temperature sensor.

- Location and local influences of override temperature sensor.

- Optimum start program parameters.

- Calibration and location of optimum start temperature sensor.

This investigation and calibration of each component can be very expensive and time consuming, yet still does not directly verify that the unit operates only when required. A far cheaper and more direct method is to datalog the amps to the fan, and the temperature in the space being served, over a period of a week or more. If the unit is observed to operate outside of the scheduled hours at any time when the space temperature is within expected parameters, an energy-wasting malfunction has been detected in the on/off functions. Once an energy-wasting malfunction is observed, the datalog data will provide clues about where to begin a search for the cause of the malfunction.

Chapters 7 and 8 describe methods of measuring the actual energy use profiles of equipment typically found in office buildings. In each case, *key operating variables* are identified and ways of measuring those variables are described.

## STEP 5: DETERMINE REQUIRED ENERGY USE

In this step of the energy-efficient operation process, the energy manager calls together the people who affect the operation of the device or system under study, and together they determine its current required profile of operation. As part of this step, the required profile of operation is compared to the actual profile of operation so that any excess energy use can be detected.

The research and practical experience upon which this operation management process is based consistently shows that many energy-consuming devices and systems use more energy than is required to perform their intended function. For example, air handlers are often found to operate excessively because their on/off schedule does not reflect the current space occupancy schedule. Office equipment often operates more than required because it is left on during nights and week-ends. The operating hours of overhead lighting often exceed the operating hours required by space occupancy. The process of defining the required profile of operation and comparing it to the actual is designed to detect these kinds of energy waste.

As explained in the preparation section above, each person who affects or determines how a device operates must participate in determining how that device currently needs to operate. For example, when discussing the appropriate weekday start-up time for an air handler, the maintenance staff may report that the unit is started at 6:00 a.m. in order to achieve comfort conditions by 7:00 a.m. However, an occupant representative may report that occupants arrive at 8:00 a.m. because of a recent change in work schedule. In this example, one hour per day of excess operation was detected by engaging the key people in defining the air handler's required operation.

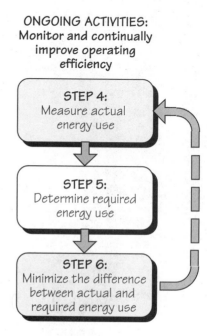

ONGOING ACTIVITIES: Monitor and continually improve operating efficiency

STEP 4: Measure actual energy use

STEP 5: Determine required energy use

STEP 6: Minimize the difference between actual and required energy use

Figure 6-5. Determining required use is the second step in the ongoing energy-efficient operations process.

Figure 6-6. The amp profile of lighting circuits can be measured with a portable datalogger. Three conductance clamps, placed around different circuit wires, are connected to the datalogger attached to the base of the panel.

## Example A: Lighting

Creating the required profile of operation is most easily accomplished by starting with the measured actual profile, questioning its characteristics and then drawing a required profile of operation on a copy of the actual operation. For example, Figure 6-7 represents the actual profile of the electrical amps to a lighting panel. The energy management team would begin by asking the following questions:

- How many switches control this lighting?
- Where are the zones controlled by the switches?
- What time does the first person arrive in each zone?
- What time does the last person leave each zone in the afternoon?
- What time does the custodial staff begin its work?
- What time is the custodial staff finished with its work?
- How many lighting zones does the custodial staff clean simultaneously?

After answering all of these questions, the energy management team may decide to drawn an amp profile for this panel that reflects when the lights are required to operate, as shown in Figure 6-8. Note that this process of beginning with the measured actual profile of operation gives the energy management team a starting point to determine whether or not any unnecessary operation is taking place, while the practice of drawing the required profile of operation over the actual profile provides a visual depiction of the quantity and time of excess energy use (the shaded area in Figure 6-8 represents excess lighting amp/hours).

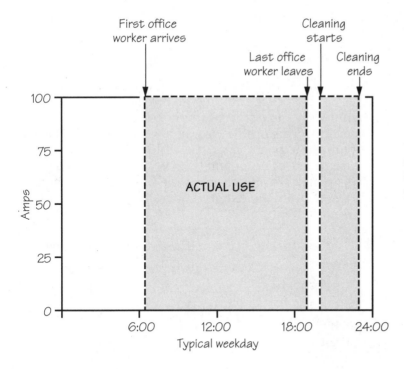

Figure 6-7. Profile of actual energy use at one electric lighting panel during a typical weekday.

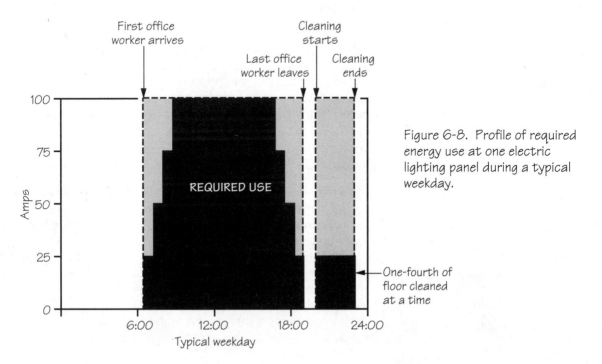

Figure 6-8. Profile of required energy use at one electric lighting panel during a typical weekday.

## Example B: Office Equipment

Figure 6-9 shows the actual amp profile of an electric panel serving office equipment. It represents the amps consumed by the office equipment on a Friday and over a weekend. This profile was reviewed by a team consisting of the energy manager, the building electrician and a representative of occupants who work in the area served by this panel. This team asked the following questions in order to draw the required operating profile for the office equipment:

1. What time do occupants arrive in the morning?
2. What time do occupants typically leave in the afternoon?
3. How many people work on Saturday, and what is their schedule?
4. What equipment consumes electricity during nights and weekends?
5. What equipment cannot be turned off?

After collecting and reviewing the answers to the above questions, the energy management team concluded that less than 20 percent of the equipment needed to operate continuously and therefore drew the required operating profile shown in Figure 6-10. The shaded area depicts the quantity of waste detected.

## Example C: Air Handler

Figure 6-11 shows a one-day actual profile of an air handler's mixed air temperature in relation to outside air temperature and supply air temperature. Knowing that a malfunction could result in significant undetected excess heating and cooling, the energy manager decided to verify the performance of this mixed air "economizer" control. This actual profile was reviewed by the energy manager, the technician familiar with the building control system and the person responsible for maintaining the air handler. This group asked the following

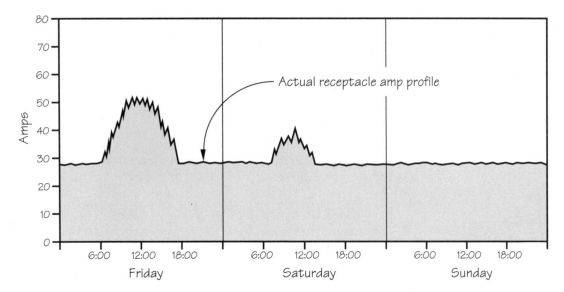

Figure 6-9. Profile of actual energy use at electric panel serving office equipment.

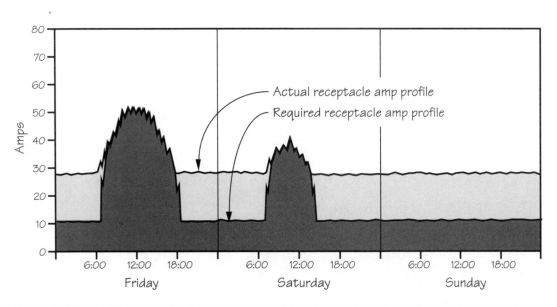

Figure 6-10. Profile of required energy use at electric panel serving office equipment.

questions to reach agreement on the required profile of operation for the mixed air temperature:

1. Is this unit intended to take in minimum outside air when the outside air temperature is higher than the return air temperature?

2. What is the minimum percent outside air required of this unit?

3. How is the energy management system programmed to control the mixed air temperature?

Based on the answers to these questions, the energy management team drew the required profile of mixed air temperature depicted in Figure 6-12. Note that the area between the mixed air temperature and the supply air temperature represents the quantity of cooling being done at the air handler. The shaded area represents the excess cooling that is taking place because of a malfunction in the mixed air control.

These examples illustrate the process of creating required profiles of operation. The key activities consist of assembling the appropriate people, reviewing the actual profile of operation and questioning whether or not that profile truly reflects the required profile of operation. Careful repetition of this process for each significant energy-consuming device will have one of two possible outcomes: either the energy management team will confirm that the device is operating as required, or the team will discover that excess energy is being consumed and that savings are possible through improved operating procedures. Both outcomes will be beneficial to achieving the goal of the energy-efficient operation process.

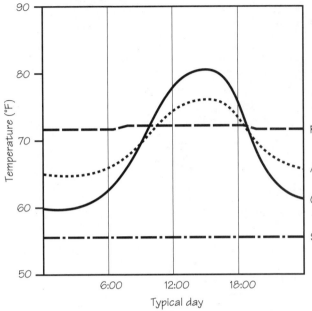

Figure 6-11. Profile of actual mixed air temperature in an air handler during a one-day period.

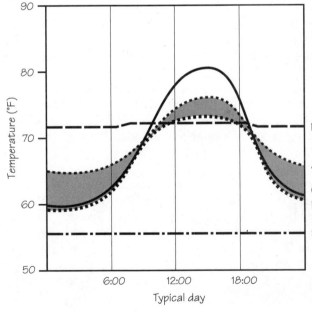

Figure 6-12. Profile of required mixed air temperature in an air handler during a one-day period.

## STEP 6: MINIMIZE THE DIFFERENCE BETWEEN ACTUAL AND REQUIRED ENERGY USE

The objective of this task is to minimize any significant differences between the actual energy use of a device or system and its required energy use. In completing this task, the energy management team proceeds through the following series of activities:

1. Estimate savings potential.

2. List optional methods for achieving savings.

3. Implement actions and remeasure.

The first activity in this process is to quantify the apparent savings potential of the documented excess energy use in order to gauge the level of effort that the item should receive. This activity is essential to keeping the energy-efficient process cost effective. These estimates of savings potential need not be extremely precise; they need only to provide a general idea of the savings potential. For example, the difference between actual and required lighting use depicted in Figure 6-8 can be estimated by quantifying the annual lighting dollars represented by Figure 6-7 (amps x volts x operating hours per week x 52 weeks per year x cost per kWh) and then visually estimating the percentage of the area under the actual lighting profile that lies outside of the required lighting profile.

Comparing the shaded area to the total area in Figure 6-8 indicates that approximately 20 percent of the actual lighting energy could be saved by eliminating the differences between the actual and required lighting operation.

A similar technique could be used to estimate the savings represented by Figure 6-10. The annual cost represented by the actual profile in Figure 6-9 could be calculated by multiplying the estimated median amps x volts x 8,760 hours per year x cost per kWh and then estimating the percent of that number that would be saved by achieving the required operation profile.

Savings achieved through correcting malfunctions in

**ONGOING ACTIVITIES:**
**Monitor and continually improve operating efficiency**

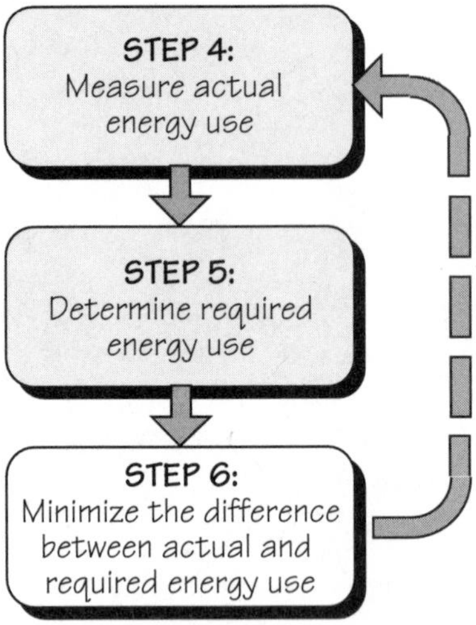

**STEP 4:**
Measure actual energy use

**STEP 5:**
Determine required energy use

**STEP 6:**
Minimize the difference between actual and required energy use

Figure 6-13. Minimizing the difference between required and actual energy use is the third step in the ongoing energy-efficient operations process.

air-handling units often require some engineering expertise, which the energy manager should seek out when necessary. However, the following example illustrates a crude method of estimating the savings that would result from correcting the mixed air control malfunction depicted in Figure 6-12. Despite the fact that this method is based on a number of rough assumptions, it provides the energy management team with an order-of-magnitude estimate of the potential savings.

The energy manager learned from an engineer that local buildings typically use 70 percent of their cooling energy to cool air and 30 percent to dehumidify air. He also decided to assume that the behavior depicted in Figure 6-11 is typical of the entire cooling season.

The space between the actual mixed air temperature line and the supply air temperature line in Figure 6-12 represents the amount of air cooling taking place; the shaded area indicates that the actual cooling exceeds the required cooling by approximately 20 percent. The excess cooling depicted in Figure 6-12 therefore represents 14 percent (20 percent x 70 percent) of the unit's total cooling.

The energy manager reviewed the capacities of all air-handling units and determined that this unit handles 40 percent of all the air circulated by the air handlers. The excess cooling depicted in Figure 6-12 now represents 5.6 percent (14 percent x 40 percent) of the entire building's cooling energy use.

The savings potential is then roughly estimated as 5.6 percent of the annual cooling costs estimated in Chapters 4 and 5 and summarized in Figure 6-2.

The general objective of this activity is to give the energy management team an order-of-magnitude idea of the savings potential of the malfunction discovered so that the team can apply the appropriate effort to achieve the potential savings. The energy manager should begin with whatever estimating skills are available and, over time, acquire additional capabilities to perform these estimates.

## Task 1:  List Optional Remedial Actions

During this activity, the energy management team lists alternative methods for minimizing the differences between the actual and required operating profiles.  It is important in this activity for the team members to resist acting on the first remedial activity that comes to mind; rather, they should review options thoughtfully and list several alternatives.  Each alternative should be weighed in light of its potential to achieve the savings, its potential to sustain the savings over time and its ease of implementation.

Methods to eliminate excess operation of overhead lighting, for example, may include such options as labeling light switches so that occupants will know which switches control their area; asking occupant managers to designate individuals to monitor lights on and lights off; and designating the custodial supervisor or night security officer as the monitor of evening lighting operation.  Similarly, options for reducing office equipment operation during unoccupied hours may include posting notices about occupant awareness programs; placing signs on key equipment to encourage workers to turn it off when it is not in use; and having supervisors of office workers designate individuals to ensure that no unnecessary equipment is left on during nights and weekends.

During this activity, the energy management team should list as many alternative remedial actions as it can and weigh each one against the criteria listed above.

## Task 2:  Implement Remedial Actions and Re-measure

After completing Task 1, the energy management team selects one or more of the remedial actions, implements those actions and then verifies the results by re-measuring the actual profile of operation and comparing it to the required profile.  The energy management team should enter into this activity with patience and an attitude of experimentation, acknowledging that "managing out" the differences between actual and required profiles of operation often takes a number of attempts.

However, the measurement procedures built into this management process allow the energy management team to see the progress made and quantify the savings achieved by various remedial actions.

## SUMMARY

A cost-effective energy-efficient operation process must be based on an understanding of which energy-consuming devices and systems are the most costly to operate, and therefore, the most important to operate efficiently. Its goal is to ensure that the largest energy users consume only as much energy as is necessary to do the job they are intended to do.

The process applied to each large energy consumer consists of three activities:

- Measure actual energy use.
- Define required energy use.
- Minimize the difference between actual and required energy use.

The process should be periodically repeated to sustain energy-efficient operation. The frequency of repetition should be based on the potential for malfunction to occur and the magnitude of excess cost that could result. Chapters 7 and 8 illustrate how this energy-efficient operation process is applied to specific uses.

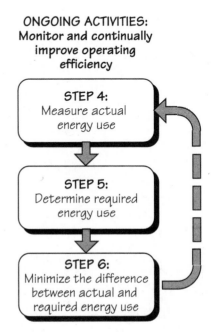

ONGOING ACTIVITIES: Monitor and continually improve operating efficiency

STEP 4: Measure actual energy use

STEP 5: Determine required energy use

STEP 6: Minimize the difference between actual and required energy use

Figure 6-14. The three steps in the ongoing energy-efficient operations process.

# CHAPTER 7

# Applying the Process to Overhead Lighting

**START-UP ACTIVITIES:**
**Identify and quantify**
**energy consumers**

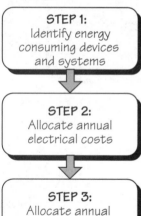

STEP 1:
Identify energy
consuming devices
and systems

STEP 2:
Allocate annual
electrical costs

STEP 3:
Allocate annual
fuel costs

Figure 7-1. Start-up activities
are the first part of the process
to achieve energy-efficient
operation of overhead lighting.

This chapter illustrates the energy-efficient operation process described in Chapter 6 by demon-strating its application to overhead lighting in an office building. The chapter begins with the three-step start-up activities (Figure 7-1) and proceeds through the three-step ongoing process. Overhead lighting is one of the clearest, least complex energy-using systems in a building. Because it generally can be understood and managed by people with little or no technical background, it is often a good place to start the process.

In this example, the facility administrator of a multi-story office building has begun the process of improving energy efficiency by forming a core energy management team. Led by the facility administrator, the team also includes a mechanical maintenance person and an electrical maintenance person. The following narrative describes their experiences as they apply the energy-efficient operation process described in this text to one category of significant energy cost—overhead lighting.

## START-UP ACTIVITIES

The energy management team began its work by identifying the facility's energy-consuming devices, estimating the annual energy dollars consumed by each

Figure 7-2. Lighting is a major energy consumer in most commercial buildings.

device (Chapters 4 and 5) and organizing this information on an energy cost allocation form (Figure 7-3). After completing these steps, the team found that overhead lighting was a significant enough energy expense item to be entered into the energy-efficient operation process.

The task of selecting the items to be operated efficiently continued as the team discussed whether lighting could be operated efficiently for the entire building at once, or whether it should be broken down into more manageable subdivisions. The facility administrator reminded the team that its goal was to start a process of periodically measuring the amount and the time of lighting energy use (operating profile) to determine whether that profile of use matched the actual need for lighting. The group recognized that measuring the

## Figure 7-3. Allocation of annual energy cost.

### ELECTRICAL USE

Item A: $0.053 per kWh (elec. cost)

| B | C | D | E | F |
|---|---|---|---|---|
| | Item | Estimated annual kWh | Annual cost | Percent of total cost |
| Constant electrical uses | E-1. Lighting | 194,700 | $10,319 | 17 % |
| | E-2. Air handling fans | 225,390 | $11,946 | 19 % |
| | E-3. Office equipment | 102,345 | $5,424 | 9 % |
| | E-4. Exhaust fans | 9,610 | $509 | 1 % |
| | E-5. Elevators | 20,900 | $1,108 | 2 % |
| | E-6. | | | |
| | E-7. Miscellaneous | 85,856 | $4,550 | 7 % |
| | E-8. Subtotals | 638,800 | $33,856 | 55 % |
| Weather-variable electrical uses | E-9. Air conditioning | 219,760 | $11,647 | 19 % |
| | E-10. | | | |
| | E-11. Subtotals | 219,760 | $11,647 | 19 % |
| | E-12. Electric totals | 858,560 | $45,081 | 74 % |

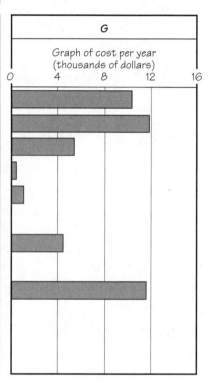

G — Graph of cost per year (thousands of dollars)

### FUEL USE

Item A: $0.452 per ccf (fuel cost)

| B | C | D | E | F |
|---|---|---|---|---|
| FUEL USE (Natural gas) | Item | Estimated annual ccf | Annual cost | Percent of total cost |
| Constant natural gas uses | F-1. Domestic hot water | 1,214 | $549 | 1 % |
| | F-2. | | | |
| | F-3. Subtotals: | 1,214 | $549 | 1 % |
| Weather-variable natural gas uses | F-4. Space heating | 34,269 | $15,489 | 25 % |
| | F-5. | | | |
| | F-6. Subtotals: | 34,269 | $15,489 | 25 % |
| | F-7. Natural gas totals | 35,483 | $16,038 | 26 % |

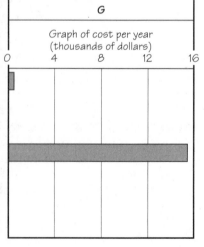

G — Graph of cost per year (thousands of dollars)

| GRAND TOTAL | All energy totals: | | $61,119 | 100 % |
|---|---|---|---|---|

electrical profile of the entire building would include all electrical consumers and therefore would provide no information on the actual behavior of lighting in individual areas. The team also recognize that measuring lighting at individual switched circuits would provide precise information on lighting behavior but would be far too time consuming to be cost effective as an ongoing management procedure. The team tentatively agreed to manage lighting at individual lighting panels and to firm up this decision after gathering more detailed information on lighting electrical distribution and lighting control.

## Collect and Organize Information

The facility administrator reminded the team that energy-efficient lighting operation was to be a team effort, and that some basic information about the lighting systems and their control should be gathered so that all members share a common understanding. The team agreed to create a file in which to store the information gathered, recognizing that they would be reviewing lighting performance once or twice a year and that a great deal of time would be saved if all relevant information was immediately available.

The energy team members knew that they needed to understand the path taken by electrical energy as it flows to the lighting system in order to decide how to subdivide lighting into manageable components and to determine the best points for measuring lighting energy. The electrical maintenance person volunteered to review the electrical riser diagram and highlight the lighting equipment (see Figure 7-4). The team noted that each floor has one lighting panel serving the overhead lights on that level.

Next, the team decided to document the path of electrical energy flow from the lighting panel on a typical floor to the overhead lighting fixtures. The electrical maintenance worker obtained a schematic floor plan upon which he located the lighting panel. He noted that each floor had seven light switches, which he also located on the plan. To verify that these switches

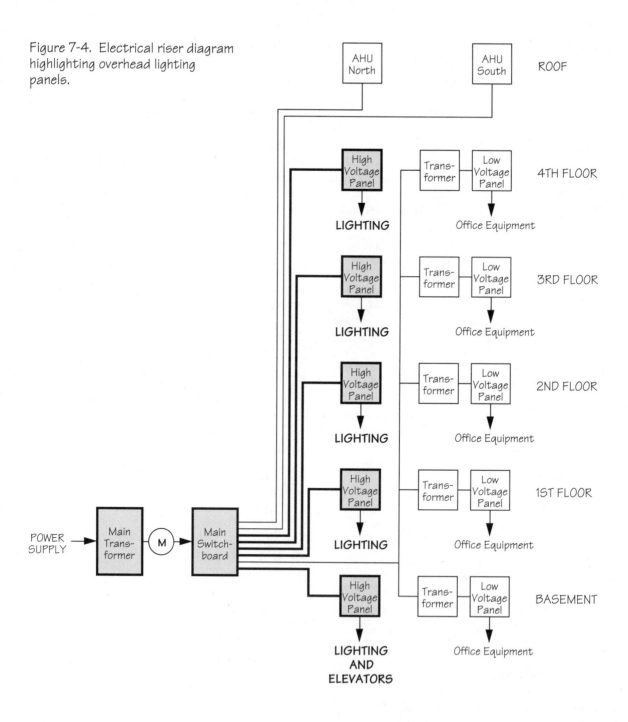

Figure 7-4. Electrical riser diagram highlighting overhead lighting panels.

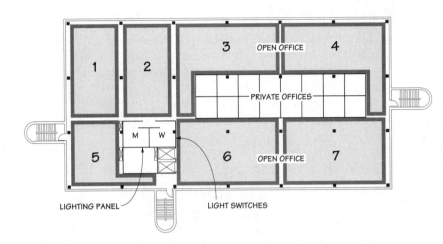

Figure 7-5. Floor plan
indicating lighting zones
controlled by separate
switches.

controlled seven distinct lighting zones, he came in early one morning and operated each light switch to document the area it controlled. These lighting "zones" were sketched on the floor plan. The team agreed that the resulting drawing (Figure 7-5) combined all of the information gathered in a form that was easily understood and could be quickly recalled when dealing with lighting issues in the future.

The electrical maintenance worker reported that the lighting in each zone could be turned on and off by the wall switch, but that an automatic "sweep" control feature in the building automation system was used to make sure that no lights stayed on all night. It was his understanding that this control was set to turn all lights off at 11:00 p.m. on weekdays. He also reported that approximately 10 percent of all overhead lighting fixtures were served by an entirely separate emergency circuit and that these lights remained on constantly.

The same worker also reported that the typical overhead lighting fixture was a 2-foot x 2-foot "U-tube" fluorescent fixture that is expected to draw 96 watts. He noted that there are approximately 145 fixtures per floor.

The facility administrator recognized that all of the information about lighting should be placed in a file from which it could be quickly retrieved whenever lighting on individual floors would be discussed in the future. Using the general file arrangement depicted in

Chapter 3, the facility manager expanded file section B-1 (*Lighting*) to include four sub-tabs, one for the overhead lighting at each floor. Information common to all lighting, such as the lighting distribution diagram and general information about fixtures and their control, was placed behind tab B-1; and the individual floor lighting schematics were placed behind the appropriate sub-tabs (Figure 7-6).

## Establish a Specific Goal

The team decided to establish a specific goal for lighting operation that could be reviewed each time lighting was discussed in order to keep the team focused on its objectives. The team began reviewing the general goals of the entire energy-efficient operation process, after affirming that the objective was to make sure that energy-consuming devices use only as much energy as is required to perform their intended function. Guided by this general principle, the team concluded that the intended function of overhead lighting fixtures is to illuminate spaces when people are present. Based on this review, the energy management team decided that its goal should be to make each lighting zone's schedule of operation match as closely as possible the schedule of occupancy in that zone.

## Decide Who Should Participate

After reviewing the information collected and the goal established, the energy management team discussed who should participate in the process of achieving and sustaining the goal. The team members recognized that the people who had the most influence on the schedule of operation for lighting fixtures were those who operated the light switches and the person who scheduled the energy management system sweep control. They noted that the lighting switches were turned on in the morning by the first occupants to arrive and that, ideally, lighting would be turned off by the last occupants to leave a lighting zone in the evening. They had learned that lighting switches were operated by

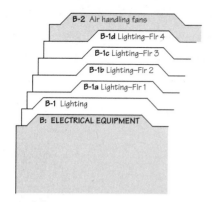

Figure 7-6. Place information behind the appropriate sub-tabs in the energy management file.

custodial staff to facilitate cleaning, and that a security guard who made rounds at night could be useful in monitoring lighting behavior and ensuring that no lighting remained on unnecessarily. The team also recognized that the schedule for the lighting sweep control was programmed by a building automation system technician.

The energy management team decided that the process of efficiently operating overhead lighting would require the cooperation of the following workers:

- someone representing early-arriving and late-departing occupants;

- the custodial supervisor;

- the security officer; and

- the building automation system technician.

After the core team had measured the actual schedule of operation of lighting on each floor, this "lighting energy management team" would be assembled to review those measurements and to determine whether the actual profile of lighting operation matched the occupants' true needs for illumination.

## ONGOING ACTIVITIES

### STEP 4: MEASURE ACTUAL LIGHTING USE

The core team members met to plan their approach to measuring lighting energy use. They recognized that the amount of electricity consumed by a light fixture in operation is determined by the characteristics of the lamps and ballasts, and therefore is not a variable that can be influenced by the people who operate lighting fixtures. They noted that the operators of overhead lighting do control when the fixtures are turned on and off. The team concluded that time of operation is the *key operating variable* that must be managed by the lighting management team to ensure that lighting consumes only as much energy as necessary.

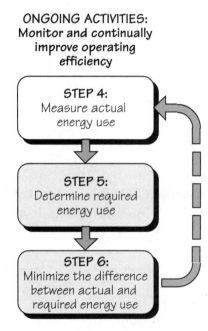

**ONGOING ACTIVITIES: Monitor and continually improve operating efficiency**

**STEP 4:** Measure actual energy use

**STEP 5:** Determine required energy use

**STEP 6:** Minimize the difference between actual and required energy use

Figure 7-7. Measuring actual use is the first step in the ongoing energy-efficient operations process.

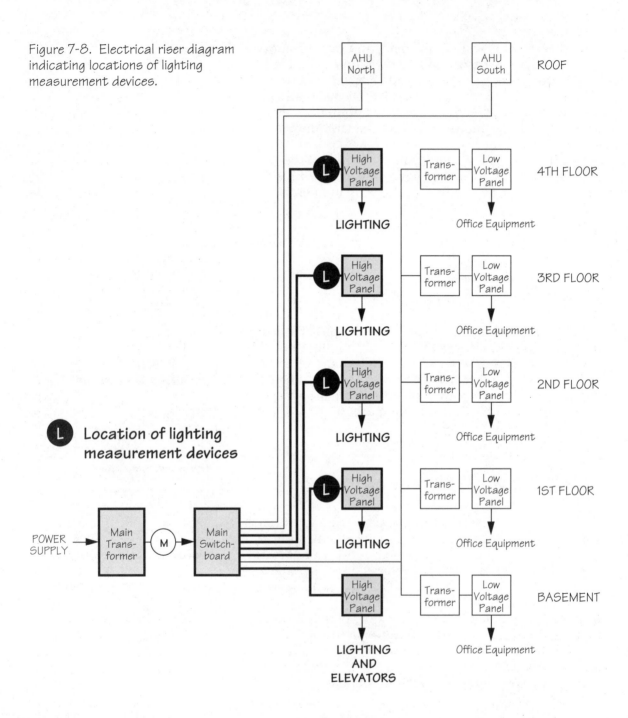

Figure 7-8. Electrical riser diagram indicating locations of lighting measurement devices.

## Determine What to Measure

The team decided that datalogging the flow of electrical amps to lighting fixtures would furnish the information they needed to manage lighting energy use. An amp profile not only would show precisely what lighting fixtures are on or off, but also would be useful in quantifying lighting energy use and cost (the average amps and hours depicted on a profile could be multiplied by voltage to determine kilowatt hours).

## Determine Where to Measure

The team members recognized that overhead lighting systems consist of many individual fixtures, which are too numerous to measure individually. They observed that it would be ideal to measure the amp profile at each of the switched circuits, but realized that this procedure would require seven measurements per floor, or 28 total measurements to record the overhead lighting for the entire four-story building.

The team concluded that measuring the profile of the amps entering the lighting panel at each floor would reduce the number of measurement points to four while still providing sufficient information to manage the overhead lighting for each floor. Team members speculated that this profile at the panel would show stepped increments each time one of the seven switches was turned on or off, allowing them to record how many zones were illuminated at what times. The points of measurement were recorded on an electrical distribution diagram and placed in the lighting file (see Figure 7-8).

## Determine How to Measure

The electrical maintenance person had acquired the use of a portable electrical current datalogger equipped with three clip-on current transformers. He proposed to attach this instrument to the three phases of current entering a lighting panel (see Figure 7-9), and indicated that the time interval at which the logger would record readings to memory was user-selectable. The group

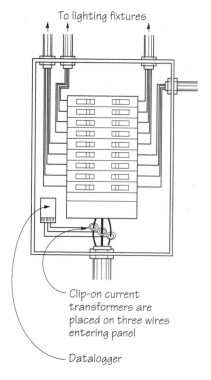

Figure 7-9. Location of datalogger within electrical panel.

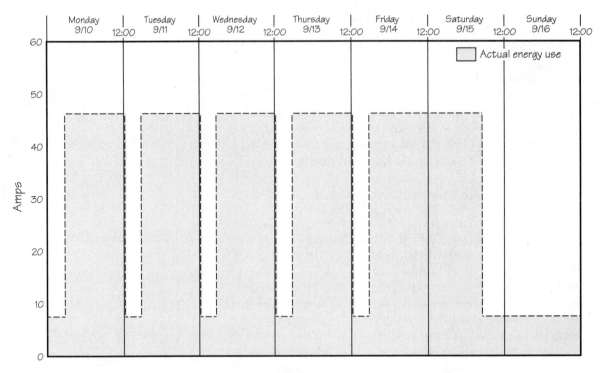

Figure 7-10. Actual energy use profile for one leg of a lighting panel during a seven-day period.

## SUMMARY OF MEASUREMENT PLAN

| | |
|---|---|
| System: | Overhead lighting |
| Key operating variable: | Time of operation |
| What to measure: | Flow of electrical amps to lighting fixtures |
| Where to measure: | Lighting panel at each floor (4 total measurements) |
| How to measure: | Portable electrical current dataloggers |
| Duration: | One full week (168 consecutive hours) |

decided that recording readings to memory every 5 minutes would be sufficiently precise for its purposes.

The team then discussed how long the measuring device should remain in place. The group members concluded that the typical use cycle of their facility was one full week (168 hours) and that the measurement period should be of that duration if they were to determine the pattern of lighting for weekdays as well as nights and weekends.

The core team concluded that its measurement process for efficiently operating lighting energy use would consist of datalogging the three phases of electrical current to the lighting panel on each of the four floors, recording every 5 minutes for at least 168 consecutive hours.

The electrical maintenance worker completed the datalogging of each panel and provided a copy of the lighting amp profile for each floor to the facility manager. These profiles (see example Figure 7-10) were then placed in the "Lighting" section of the energy management file, behind the sub-tabs provided for each floor.

## STEP 5: DETERMINE REQUIRED LIGHTING USE

After completing the measurements of the actual electrical use profiles for the lighting panels, the energy management team decided to begin with the fourth floor in initiating the process of defining the required energy use profile.

In keeping with the previous discussion concerning who should participate in managing lighting, the core team assembled a "fourth-floor lighting management team" that included the person who typically is the first to arrive at the fourth floor in the morning—the manager of the personnel on the fourth floor, who often worked late herself and could answer questions concerning the departure pattern of fourth floor offices workers. This lighting management team also included the custodial supervisor, who understood the work patterns of evening cleaning crews; and the security officer who typically made rounds of the building twice on weeknights.

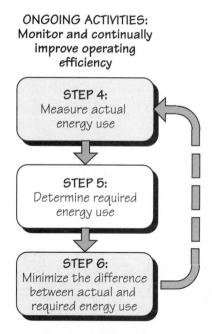

ONGOING ACTIVITIES: Monitor and continually improve operating efficiency

**STEP 4:** Measure actual energy use

**STEP 5:** Determine required energy use

**STEP 6:** Minimize the difference between actual and required energy use

Figure 7-11. Determining required use is the second step in the ongoing energy-efficient operations process.

The facility administrator prepared the group members to discuss the lighting patterns by reviewing the fourth-floor lighting schematic plan with them (see Figure 7-5) and showing how the seven light switches near the elevators controlled the seven lighting zones on the plan. He also used the plan to indicate the location of the lighting panel and explained that all overhead lighting received its electrical energy from that panel. The electrical maintenance person then explained the datalogging process and showed the group the sketch in Figure 7-8 so that they all understood the origin of the actual lighting amp profile.

The facility manager then referred to the specific lighting management goal created by the core team and informed the full team that its goal was to "make each lighting zone's schedule of operation match as closely as possible the schedule of occupancy in that zone."

The facility administrator had prepared an overhead transparency of the actual fourth-floor lighting amp profile (Figure 7-10), which was projected onto a screen for the group to review. Referring to the specific lighting management goal, the facility manager noted that the task of this group was to determine whether this profile of operation matched the schedule of occupancy of the fourth floor. He suggested that a profile of required operation be drawn over this profile of actual operation. If, at the end of that exercise, the actual and required profiles nearly matched, the group would have affirmed that this lighting is operating efficiently and that no remedial action is required. If, however, there was a considerable mismatch between actual and required profiles, the team would do whatever it could to minimize or eliminate excess operation of lighting on the fourth floor.

The facility administrator began by asking the group if the profile of lighting start-up in the morning was consistent with space occupancy. He observed that the plots show that all seven switches are turned on at the same time, indicating that people from all seven work zones arrive together, sometime between 5:30 and 6:00 a.m. on weekdays. However, the person who typically arrives at that time daily said that he is usually the only one on the floor until approximately 7:30 a.m. and that in his opinion all seven zones are not occupied until 8:00 a.m. He indicated that although his work station is in zone 7, he turns on all seven light switches because there is no indication of which switch controls which zone. This worker added that he was unaware that the cost of operating this lighting was significant. The group agreed that the morning start-up lighting profile should consist of a series of seven steps, reflecting when the seven zones become occupied, as opposed to one large step occurring when the first person arrives.

The facility administrator then called the group's attention to the shape of the profile at the end of the typical weekdays. The manager of the workers on the fourth floor said that several of the lighting zones are typically vacated by 4:30 p.m. and that on most days the office workers have vacated the entire floor by 6:30 p.m. In her opinion, a profile that truly reflected zone occupancy would show a series of declining steps beginning at 4:30 p.m. and progressing to 0 amps by approximately 6:30 p.m. She further indicated that zones 1 and 5 are commonly occupied on Saturdays from 8:00 a.m. to 12 noon and that Sunday occupancy is very rare.

The custodial supervisor reported that the custodial staff typically finds all lights on when they arrive on the floor at approximately 7:00 p.m. and that they usually complete their work between 9:00 and 9:30 p.m. They do not switch the lights off because they understood that the lights were turned off by an automatic timer. When asked if the cleaning crews needed the entire floor lit to complete their work, the supervisor replied that their common practice is to empty wastebaskets for the entire floor and then vacuum the entire floor, in which case all lighting needed to be on until the work was completed. He added, however, that it would be possible to have the lights off on one-half of the floor while the other half is being cleaned and then reverse this process, resulting in a 50 percent lighting reduction during cleaning hours. The team then decided that approximately 25 amps of lighting were required between the hours of 7:00 p.m. and 9:30 p.m.

The lighting team then asked why the lighting was being turned off at midnight. The technician who programs the energy management system "sweep control" answered that the timer was originally set to turn off lights at 11:00 p.m. but that this scheduled "off" time had been moved to midnight eight months ago to accommodate a special carpet cleaning project. Apparently it had not occurred to anyone to request that the technician reset the timer schedule to 11:00 p.m.

The team noted that approximately 8 amps of lighting apparently never went off and that the lighting failed to go off on Friday night. They also noted that the lighting sweep apparently allowed lights to stay on until 5:00 p.m. on Saturday. The group agreed that this plot of lighting amps indicates lighting operation in excess of the actual needs of space occupants.

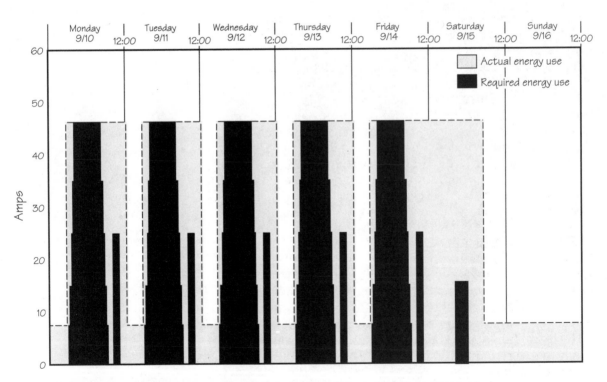

Figure 7-12. Required energy use profile for lighting panel during a seven-day period.

As a result of these conversations, the team drew Figure 7-12, which shows the profile of required lighting operation agreed to by the team superimposed on the actual profile of lighting operation.

## STEP 6:  MINIMIZE THE DIFFERENCE BETWEEN ACTUAL AND REQUIRED LIGHTING USE

### Quantify Savings Potential

The fourth-floor lighting energy management team members recognized that they needed to quantify the difference between the actual and required operating profiles in order to determine how much effort to expend in trying to eliminate the waste they had documented.  The team recognized that it did not need a precise estimate of the savings potential; a general estimate would be sufficient.

The group decided to begin by estimating the dollars of electricity represented by the actual profile in order to get a preliminary understanding of the magnitude of dollars in question.  First, the group calculated the actual amp hours of lighting consumed during the week.  The total amps consumed when all lighting is operating equals the sum of the amps in the three conductors entering the panel.  Figure 7-10 represents one of the three lines; the other two were nearly identical in shape and peaked at 45 amps and 47 amps, respectively.  The total is calculated as follows:

Total amps = 45 + 46 + 47

Total amps = 138

The team then calculcated the total hours at full operation in the week to be approximately 108 hours, and observed that for the remaining 60 hours per week the lights operated at 8 amps on one line only.  Assuming that the week shown in Figure 7-10 is typical of all 52 weeks in the year and noting that the panels operated at 277 volts, the team used the following formula to represent the annual kilowatt hours (kWh) of actual lighting on the fourth floor:

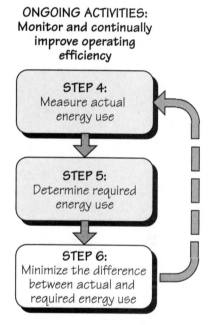

ONGOING ACTIVITIES:
Monitor and continually improve operating efficiency

**STEP 4:**
Measure actual energy use

**STEP 5:**
Determine required energy use

**STEP 6:**
Minimize the difference between actual and required energy use

Figure 7-13. Minimizing the difference between required and actual energy use is the third step in the ongoing energy-efficient operations process.

kWh per year =

$$\frac{138 \text{ amps} \times 277 \text{ volts} \times 108 \text{ hrs/wk} \times 52 \text{ wks/yr}}{1000 \text{ watts per kilowatt}}$$

$$+ \frac{8 \text{ amps} \times 277 \text{ volts} \times 60 \text{ hrs/wk} \times 52 \text{ wks/yr}}{1000 \text{ watts per kilowatt}}$$

kWh per year = 221,591 kWh per year

The facility manager then reported that the cost of electricity was $0.05 per kilowatt hour. Multiplying this number by the kWh per year above resulted in an annual cost for lighting on the fourth floor:

Cost per year = 221,591 kWh per year x $0.05 per kWh

Cost per year = $11,080

The group then reviewed Figure 7-12 and concluded that approximately 35 percent of the area under the actual profile would be saved if the lighting could be operated on the required profile. The group calculated the potential savings as follows:

Savings = $11,080 x .30

Savings = $3,300

The team concluded that this potential savings was significant enough to warrant continued team efforts. Several members of the team observed that this process had offered an opportunity not only to save energy dollars, but also to reduce an apparently needless waste of natural resources and the environmental degradation that accompanies energy use.

## Identify Strategies and Take Action

Based on the information thus far collected, the team began a list of actions that could be taken to bring the actual lighting amp profile more into line with the required amp profile. The following actions were suggested:

- Number the lighting switches and key them to a map showing the areas controlled by each switch, similar to Figure 7-5. Mount this map on the wall next to the switches. Have the fourth-floor office manager request that all employees learn which switch controls their zone and encourage the first workers in and last workers out to use the wall switches.

- Have the programmer for the lighting "sweep" control schedule the off command for 10:30 p.m. on weekdays.

- Have the lighting sweep control and the electrician work together to determine why all lights do not go off at night and why lights stay on Friday night.

- Instruct custodial staff to clean one-half of the floor at a time and teach them how to use the lighting switches, using the lighting switch zone map. The custodial supervisor should tell custodial staff to expect that lighting will be off when they arrive on the floor, and that they should illuminate only one-half of the floor at a time and switch lights off as they leave.

The team agreed that the lighting sweep control should serve as a backup in the event that lighting has not been manually switched off previously. It should not be relied upon as the primary means of turning lights off.

The group agreed that all the actions suggested should be implemented and further agreed to reconvene in a month, at which time new readings of the actual amp profile would be reviewed.

The team met a month later and reported the following:

- The programmer of the lighting sweep control reported that lighting was staying on on Friday nights because an error in the program. He also reported that he had moved the off command to 10:30 p.m. on weekdays and 2:00 p.m. on Saturdays.

- The electrical maintenance worker reported that the lighting relay controlling one of the zones had failed and therefore would not turn the lights off despite the operation of the light switch or the sweep controller. He reported that this relay had been replaced.

- The custodial supervisor reported that the custodial crew found it acceptable to activate the lighting one-half of the floor at a time. He added that the crew was considering activating one-third or even one-fourth of the lighting at a time in order to further reduce the lighting used during cleaning periods.

- The fourth-floor office manager reported that she had instructed all staff in the location of lighting zones and lighting switches and had requested that the occupants in each area operate the lighting as coincident as possible with occupancy.

The group reviewed the most recent actual profile of fourth floor lighting amps, as shown in Figure 7-14. While the members noted that some early arrivals appeared to be turning lights on in several zones unnecessarily, it was generally agreed that they had made substantial progress toward their goal of making each lighting zone's schedule of operation match as closely as possible the schedule of occupancy in that zone.

The team then discussed what actions could be taken to sustain the savings achieved. The following items were noted:

- The manager of the fourth floor staff decided to publicize the savings achieved in order to give them some deserved recognition and encourage their continued efforts.

- The custodial supervisor decided that he should recognize the fourth floor cleaning crew's contribution to this savings effort.

- The entire team recognized that future changes in work schedules, turnover in both office staff and

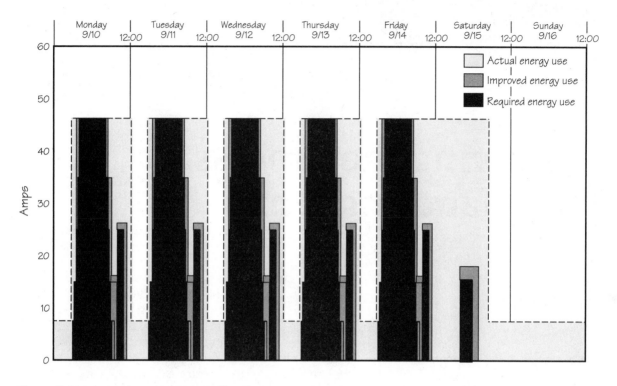

Figure 7-14. Actual energy use profile after corrective action for lighting panel during a seven-day period.

custodial staff, and the possibility of control malfunctions will require that they regularly reconvene in the future to repeat the process of reviewing profiles of actual lighting operation and compare that profile to a current definition of required operation.

• Based on the magnitude of savings or waste possible and the likelihood of significant change in either the required or actual profile of operation, the team agreed to meet twice a year to briefly repeat this process and ensure that no significant energy waste is occurring because of unnecessary lighting operation.

# CHAPTER 8

# Applying the Process to Air-Handling Units

Figure 8-1. Air handlers can waste a significant amount of energy unless a process is in place to ensure efficient operation.

This chapter illustrates how the process for achieving operating efficiency described in Chapter 6 can be applied to achieving operating efficiency in air-handling units. Unlike overhead lighting, discussed in the previous chapter, air-handling units require a certain degree of technical understanding to identify malfuctions and savings opportunities. Facility managers, assisted by people with mechanical/electrical background can address these issues. If the expertise does not exist within the organization, it should be obtained from outside. People should be assembled who can identify how the air handler is intended to operate, and how to measure its actual operation. Possible participants include the equipment operator, the design engineer and the control contractor.

In this example, the facility administrator in a multi-story office building has begun the process of achieving operating efficiency by forming a core energy management team consisting of himself, a mechanical maintenance person and an electrical maintenance person. The following narrative describes their experiences as they apply the operating efficiency process to the building's air-handling units.

# START-UP ACTIVITIES

The energy management team began its work by identifying the energy-consuming devices in the building (Chapter 3) and then estimating the annual energy dollars consumed by each device (Chapters 4 and 5). The team organized this information on an energy cost allocation form similar to Figure 8-3. After completing these preliminary activities, the team found air conditioning and air-handling fans accounted for a significant amount of the facility's annual energy dollars. Because this energy is consumed at the two large rooftop ventilating/cooling units, the team decided it was important to ensure that these units operated efficiently.

Previously gathered information indicated that the two rooftop units were identical; each had a fan capacity of 30,000 cfm and was equipped with direct expansion cooling.

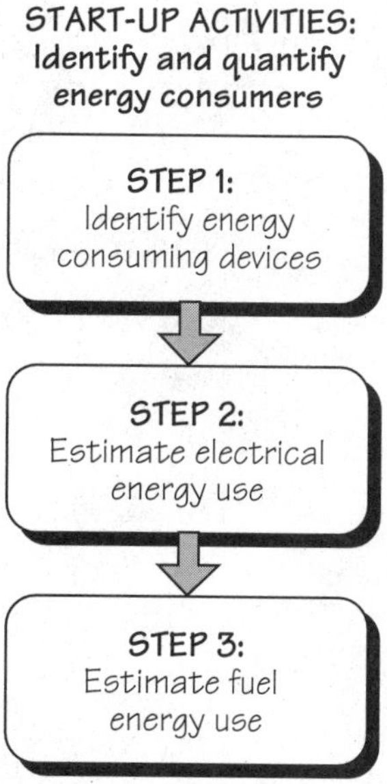

## Collect and Organize Information

The facility administrator reminded the team members that they were beginning a long-term commitment to sustaining the operating efficiency of their air-handling units, and that the procedures they devised to sustain operating efficiency would be repeated periodically for the life of the building. For that reason, the team agreed to create a file in which to store the information collected, recognizing that a great deal of time would be saved if all relevant information was immediately available each time the performance of the air handlers was reviewed in the future.

The energy team first decided to document the occupant areas served by each of the two air-handling units to help determine who should be involved in any future discussions about the appropriate operating schedule and the conditions that should be maintained for each unit. The mechanical maintenance worker noted that each air handler served one-half of each of the building's four floors. He sketched the boundaries of the area

START-UP ACTIVITIES:
Identify and quantify
energy consumers

STEP 1:
Identify energy
consuming devices

STEP 2:
Estimate electrical
energy use

STEP 3:
Estimate fuel
energy use

Figure 8-2. Start-up activities are the first part of the process to achieve energy-efficient operation in air-handling units.

Figure 8-3. Allocation of annual energy cost.

## ELECTRICAL USE

Item A: $0.053 per kWh (elec. cost)

| B | C | D | E | F | G |
|---|---|---|---|---|---|
| | Item | Estimated annual kWh | Annual cost | Percent of total cost | Graph of cost per year (thousands of dollars) |
| Constant electrical uses | E-1. Lighting | 194,700 | $10,319 | 17 % | |
| | E-2. Air handling fans | 225,390 | $11,946 | 19 % | |
| | E-3. Office equipment | 102,345 | $5,424 | 9 % | |
| | E-4. Exhaust fans | 9,610 | $509 | 1 % | |
| | E-5. Elevators | 20,900 | $1,108 | 2 % | |
| | E-6. | | | | |
| | E-7. Miscellaneous | 85,856 | $4,550 | 7 % | |
| | E-8. Subtotals | 638,800 | $33,856 | 55 % | |
| Weather-variable electrical uses | E-9. Air conditioning | 219,760 | $11,647 | 19 % | |
| | E-10. | | | | |
| | E-11. Subtotals | 219,760 | $11,647 | 19 % | |
| | E-12. Electric totals | 858,560 | $45,081 | 74 % | |

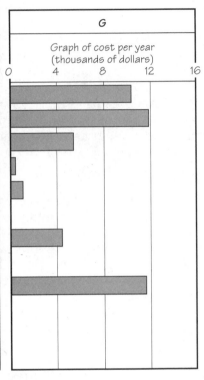

## FUEL USE

Item A: $0.452 per ccf (fuel cost)

| B | C | D | E | F | G |
|---|---|---|---|---|---|
| FUEL USE (Natural gas) | Item | Estimated annual ccf | Annual cost | Percent of total cost | Graph of cost per year (thousands of dollars) |
| Constant natural gas uses | F-1. Domestic hot water | 1,214 | $549 | 1 % | |
| | F-2. | | | | |
| | F-3. Subtotals: | 1,214 | $549 | 1 % | |
| Weather-variable natural gas uses | F-4. Space heating | 34,269 | $15,489 | 25 % | |
| | F-5. | | | | |
| | F-6. Subtotals: | 34,269 | $15,489 | 25 % | |
| | F-7. Natural gas totals | 35,483 | $16,038 | 26 % | |

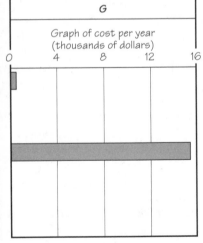

| GRAND TOTAL | All energy totals: | | $61,119 | 100 % |
|---|---|---|---|---|

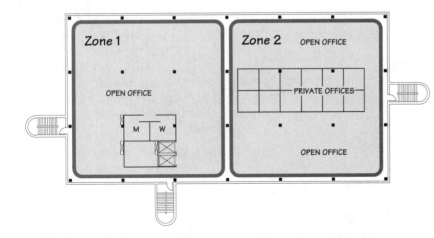

Figure 8-4. Schematic floor plan of an office building showing the area served by each air handling unit.

served by each air handler on a schematic floor plan similar to Figure 8-4.

Next, the team decided to prepare a schematic sketch of the air flow path from the rooftop units to the spaces they serve. Based on the experience of the mechanical maintenance worker and a review of the mechanical drawings, the team produced Figure 8-5 to represent the general arrangement of the most significant components. The mechanical maintenance person also prepared a schematic sketch of the rooftop units (Figure 8-6), anticipating that future discussions about how the units are intended to operate would be facilitated if all of the team members could quickly come to a general understanding of the units' general configuration.

The team recognized that in order to determine whether the air handlers were operating as intended, they should gather some basic information on their operation and control. Using Figures 8-5 and 8-6, along with the "Sequence of Operation" found in the building construction specifications, the team set down the following key operating characteristics:

- The air-handling units are intended to go on and off on a daily schedule programmed into the air handler control timer.

- Air-handling units can automatically come back on during a programmed "off" period if the temperature at the override thermostat (see Figure 8-5) exceeds the high limit or low limit programmed into the air handler controller. This automatic feature is intended to prevent the building from becoming exceedingly hot or exceedingly cold during programmed "off" (unoccupied) periods.

- The unit is intended to supply air at 55°F to variable-air-volume (VAV) boxes in both typical interior and exterior spaces. Thermostats in those spaces determine the quantity of 55°F air admitted to the room.

- Heating is provided at exterior spaces by perimeter radiation controlled by the room thermostat. This thermostat is intended to minimize the cooling air coming from the variable-air-volume (VAV) box before activating the perimeter radiation, in order to prevent simultaneous heating and cooling. No heating is required for interior spaces.

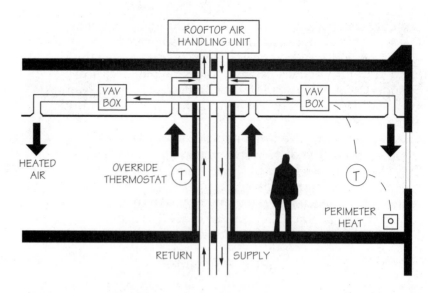

Figure 8-5. Schematic of the air flow path from the rooftop units to the spaces served.

- The outside air and return air dampers at the rooftop unit (see Figure 8-6) are intended to blend those two air streams to achieve 55°F whenever the temperature outside is below 55°F; to admit 100 percent outside air when the outside temperature is between 55°F and 72°F; and to admit 15 percent outside air when the outside temperature is above 72°F. This "economizer" function is intended to maintain the coolest mixed air possible during the cooling season in order to minimize the work required by the direct expansion cooling system.

- The supply fan is equipped with inlet vanes to modulate the quantity of air allowed into the fan in response to the varying amount of air called for by the variable-air-volume boxes. These inlet vanes are controlled by a pressure sensor in the supply air duct.

- The direct expansion cooling system is controlled by a temperature sensor in the supply air duct that cycles the cooling compressor as required to maintain a supply air temperature of 55°F.

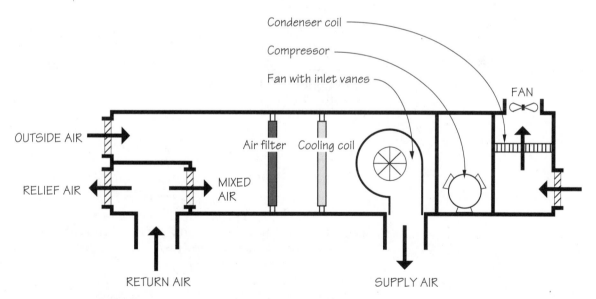

Figure 8-6. Schematic of rooftop air handling units.

While the energy management team members realized that more information on the air handlers and their function may be required in the future, they decided that they had gathered sufficient information to begin the process of analyzing how the system actually operates.

The facility administrator recognized that the information gathered about the air-handling system should be placed in a file from which it could be quickly retrieved whenever the air-handling units were discussed. Using the general file arrangement depicted in Figure 3-5, the team could place information about the electrical consumption of the air-handling fans in Section B-2, and information about the electrical consumption of the cooling compressors in Section B-3. The team created two sub-tabs for each of these sections, one for each air handler (see Figure 8-7).

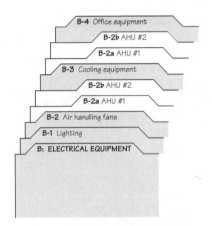

Figure 8-7. Place information behind the appropriate sub-tabs in the energy management file.

### Establish a Specific Goal

The team decided to set down a specific goal for the operating efficiency of the air-handling units that could be reviewed each time the air handlers were discussed in order to keep the team focused on its objectives. After reviewing the operating characteristics listed above, the team speculated on which operating and control functions could have an energy-wasting malfunction that would not cause occupant discomfort and therefore might go undetected. The team concluded that every operating and control function could have an undetected energy-wasting malfunction. For example:

- A failure in the on/off timer or in the override control could cause the air handler to operate undetected during unoccupied hours.

- A malfunction in the supply air control could result in an unnecessarily low supply air temperature, causing excess cooling and dehumidification. The variable-air-volume boxes would prevent the spaces from overcooling.

- Control failures could result in simultaneous heating and cooling at perimeter spaces, wasting energy without causing discomfort.

- Failure in the mixed air "economizer" control could result in unnecessary and undetected excess operation of the direct expansion cooling system.

- Failure of the fan inlet vane control system could result in an unnecessarily high duct static pressure and undetected excess electricity consumption by the fan motor.

Recognizing that the general goal for the operating efficiency process is to make sure that the devices use only as much energy as is required to perform their intended function, the team decided on the following specific goals for the air-handling units:

- The operating schedule for the air handler fans must match as closely as possible the needs of the building occupants.

- The mixed air "economizer" control must function as intended.

- The supply air temperature must be maintained at the highest acceptable temperature.

- Unnecessary simultaneous heating and cooling must be avoided at the perimeter spaces.

## Decide Who Should Participate

Upon reviewing the information gathered and the goals established, the energy management team discussed who should participate in the process of achieving and sustaining the efficient operation of their air-handling units. After discussing which workers influence when the air handlers need to run and which workers influence how the systems actually run, the team concluded that the following people needed to participate:

- the facility administrator;

- a mechanical maintenance person;

- an electrical maintenance person;

- certain department managers and the custodial manager, who had knowledge of building occupancy patterns; and

- the control technician who established the program for the air handler controller.

The team decided to proceed with gathering additional information and measuring actual performance and to meet later with the significant influencers of air handler operation as required.

# ONGOING ACTIVITIES

## STEP 4: MEASURE ACTUAL AIR-HANDLING UNIT OPERATION

The core team met to plan its approach to measuring the performance of the air-handling units. The team members decided to use their list of undetected waste possibilities documented above as a guide to their measurement strategy.

### Determine What to Measure

The *key operating variables* in an air-handling unit that influence energy-efficient operation are:

- Fan on and off schedule

- Mixed air temperature ("economizer" operation)

- Supply air temperature

- Possibility of simultaneous heating and cooling of perimeter spaces

The team decided that the flow of electricity (amps) to the air-handling fans must be measured to determine the air-handling units' on/off schedule.

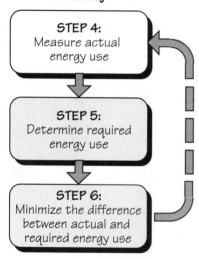

**ONGOING ACTIVITIES:**
Monitor and continually improve operating efficiency

**STEP 4:**
Measure actual energy use

**STEP 5:**
Determine required energy use

**STEP 6:**
Minimize the difference between actual and required energy use

Figure 8-8. Measuring actual use is the first step in the ongoing energy-efficient operation process.

The operation of the mixed air control would require the simultaneous measurement of the outside, return and mixed air temperatures. The analysis of these profiles would show whether the mixed air control is behaving as intended and whether the economizer cycle is working effectively.

The maintenance staff must check the position of the variable-air-volume box dampers at exterior spaces during the heating season to verify that no excess simultaneous heating and cooling is taking place.

## Determine Where to Measure

The electrical maintenance worker explained that electrical power to the air-handling fan is provided from a motor control center in the electrical room below each rooftop unit. This would be a convenient place to locate the measuring device.

The mechanical maintenance worker confirmed that the access panels on the rooftop unit would allow access

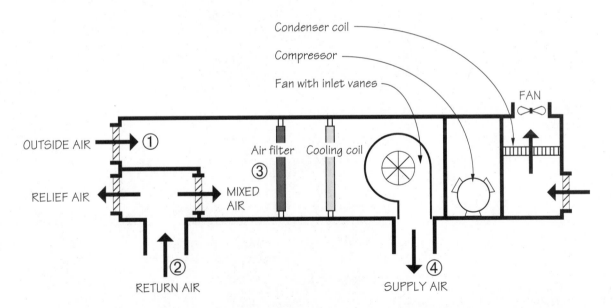

Figure 8-9. Placement of temperature dataloggers in air-handling unit. Numbers indicate logger locations.

to the outside air, return air and mixed air chambers. In addition, a measurement device could be placed in the ductwork downstream of the supply fan to record the supply air temperature (see Figure 8-9).

It was decided that datalogging at all locations should take place simultaneously for a minimum of seven continuous days so that the energy use profiles could be observed for nights and weekends as well as weekdays.

## SUMMARY OF MEASUREMENT PLAN

| | |
|---|---|
| System: | Air-Handling Units |
| Key operating variables: | Time of fan operation<br>Mixed air temperature control<br>Supply air temperature<br>When heating and cooling are supplied to perimeter spaces |
| People involved: | The facility administrator<br>A mechanical maintenance person<br>An electrical maintenance person<br>Certain department managers and the custodial staff manager<br>The electronic technician who programs the air handler controller |
| What to measure: | Flow of electrical amps to air handling fans<br>Mixed air, supply air, outside air, and return air temperatures |
| Where to measure: | Electric conductor to air-handling fans<br>Outside air chamber<br>Return air chamber<br>Mixed air chamber<br>In ductwork downstream of of supply fan |
| How to measure: | Portable electrical current datalogger<br>Portable temperature dataloggers |
| Duration: | One full week (168 consecutive hours)<br>All measurements must be simultaneous |

## How to Measure

The schedule of fan operation could be measured by using a portable electric current datalogger to obtain a profile of amps to the fan motor. This amp profile was expected to show some daily variation, indicating whether or not the inlet vanes were varying the quantity of air as intended.

Portable temperature dataloggers could be used to record the mixed air, supply air, return air and outside air temperatures. In all cases, the measurements must be taken simultaneously during the same seven-day period.

## STEP 5: DETERMINE REQUIRED OPERATION OF AN AIR-HANDLING UNIT

The team began the energy-efficient operation process by reviewing the actual profile of the amps to the fan motor on one of the air-handling units (see Figure 8-11) in order to determine whether the unit's operating schedule was appropriate for the occupancy pattern. To verify the current occupancy pattern, the team requested two managers who could define the typical arrival and departure patterns of building occupants.

The electrical maintenance person provided the team members with copies of Figure 8-11. They began by discussing the time when the air-handling unit was required to begin operation in the morning. They noted that the unit typically started at 5:00 a.m. on Monday through Friday, at 7:00 a.m. on Saturday and at 11:00 a.m. on Sunday. The managers told the group that there is usually no significant occupancy before 7:30 a.m. on weekdays or before 8:00 a.m. on Saturdays, and that generally no one works on Sundays. The mechanical maintenance person said that the unit was started at 5:00 a.m. on weekdays based on the assumption that occupants arrived at 7:00 a.m. and that it would take two hours for the building to achieve comfort conditions after being shut down at night. The group agreed that the building did not need to achieve comfort conditions

ONGOING ACTIVITIES:
Monitor and continually improve operating efficiency

STEP 4:
Measure actual energy use

STEP 5:
Determine required energy use

STEP 6:
Minimize the difference between actual and required energy use

Figure 8-10. Determining required use is the second step in the ongoing energy-efficient operation process.

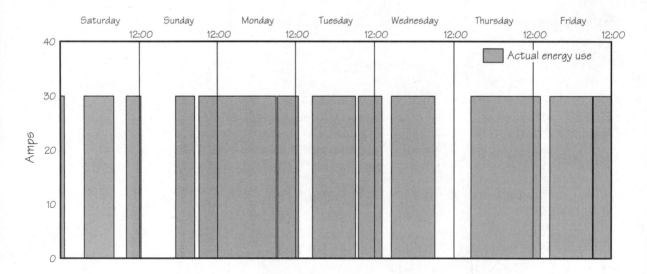

Figure 8-11. Actual energy use profile for air handler fans during a seven-day period.

until 7:30 a.m. and further agreed that the assumption of a two hour warm-up/cool-down period should be verified.

The team placed temperature dataloggers in key spaces to determine how hot or cold they get during unoccupied hours and how long it takes to achieve comfort conditions once the air-handling units start up in the morning. They were surprised to discover that conditions often stayed within the comfort range despite unit shutdown, and they observed that it never took more than 45 minutes after start-up to recover comfortable conditions. The team agreed to start the air handling units at 6:30 a.m. instead of at 5:00 a.m.

The group then discussed the time at which the air-handling unit could be shut off in the afternoon. The managers indicated that most building occupants departed at 5:00 p.m., with approximately 10 percent remaining until 6:00 p.m. The custodial manager said that his staff typically worked from 6:00 p.m. until 9:00 p.m. and that they had found working conditions acceptable with the air handlers off. The team agreed that the air-handling units were required to operate until 5:30

p.m. on weekdays. The managers noted that few, if any, workers occupied the building after noon on Saturday and that therefore the air handler could be off at that time.

The team reviewed the actual measured on/off pattern of the air-handling unit and observed frequent operation during unoccupied hours. The mechanical maintenance staff reported that the timer that controlled the air handler fan schedule was currently programmed to operate the unit from 5:00 a.m. to 6:00 p.m. on weekdays, from 7:00 a.m. to 4:00 p.m. on Saturday and from 11:00 a.m. to 3:00 p.m. on Sunday. The staff concluded that the frequent operation outside of these scheduled "on" times indicated a possible malfunction in the "override" control feature that can operate the unit during "off" periods if the space temperatures become too hot or too cold. It was agreed that the thermostat that controlled this function should be investigated.

The team observed that the fan amp draw profile was almost a flat line any time the fan was in operation. This suggested an apparent malfunction in the inlet vane/pressure sensor control, which is intended to vary the amount of air moved by the fan (and thereby the amount of work done by the fan) in response to variations in need to provide cooling.

The team members next decided to review the actual profile of the return air, mixed air, outside air and supply air temperatures in order to determine whether the supply air and mixed air were being controlled appropriately. They created Figure 8-12, which shows datalogs of these temperatures superimposed on one another for the hours during which the fan operated on one typical weekday.

The mechanical maintenance worker noted that the supply air temperature was being maintained at approximately 52°F instead of the 55°F he expected, resulting in an extra 3°F of cooling. He also pointed out that during the morning hours shown in Figure 8-12, the mixed air temperature should have coincided with the outside air temperature, indicating 100 percent outside air "economizing." However, the plot shows that the unit is actually admitting approximately 40 percent outside air

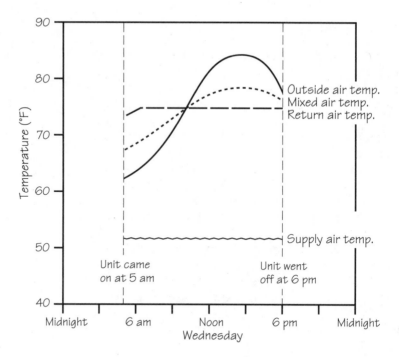

Figure 8-12. Profiles of actual temperatures recorded in an air-handling unit.

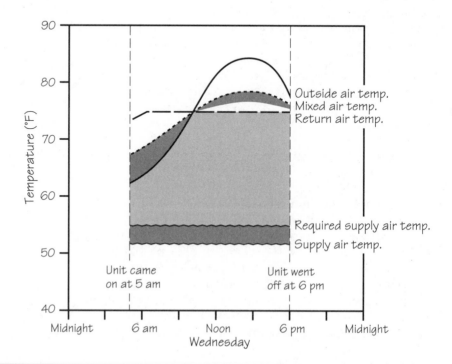

Figure 8-13. Profiles of actual and required temperatures in an air-handling unit. The light shaded area shows the required amount of cooling, and the dark shaded area shows excess cooling taking place as a result of malfunctions.

constantly. Figure 8-13 was created to show the required quantity of cooling (light shaded area) and to show the excess cooling taking place as a result of previously undetected malfunctions (dark shaded area). This figure indicates that approximately 20 percent excess cooling was taking place during the day represented by Figure 8-13.

The team agreed that the calibration of the supply air temperature sensor and the function of the mixed air controller should be investigated.

## STEP 6: MINIMIZE THE DIFFERENCE BETWEEN ACTUAL AND REQUIRED OPERATION

### Quantify Savings Potential

The energy team made a copy of the actual fan amp profile (Figure 8-11) and superimposed on it the required operating profile agreed to by the energy team (Figure 8-15). The darker shaded areas represent the unnecessary excess hours of fan operation. The team members calculated that the actual number of hours of operation for the period of datalogging was 122 hours per week. They also calculated that their required schedule called for 65 hours per week of operation. Therefore, for the datalogged period the air handler operated 57 hours per week more than necessary which represents an 88 percent excess operation. This number represents not only 88 percent more electrical energy consumed by the fans, but also significant excess operation by the direct expansion cooling system.

The group decided to estimate the dollars of electricity represented by the excess fan operation. The fan draws approximately 30 amps and was observed to operate an excess 57 hours per week. Assuming that this excess operation occurred for all 52 weeks in a year and using their electrical cost of $0.05 per kWh, the team performed the following calculation:

$$\text{Cost} = \frac{30 \text{ amps} \times 460 \text{ volts} \times 3 \times 57 \text{ hrs/wk} \times 52 \text{ wks/yr} \times \$0.05/\text{kWh}}{1000 \text{ w/kW}}$$

$$\text{Cost} = \$3,542 \text{ per year}$$

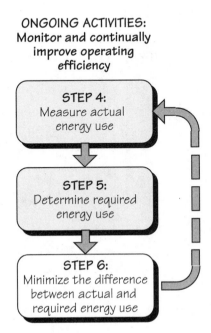

ONGOING ACTIVITIES: Monitor and continually improve operating efficiency

**STEP 4:** Measure actual energy use

**STEP 5:** Determine required energy use

**STEP 6:** Minimize the difference between actual and required energy use

Figure 8-14. Minimizing the difference between required and actual energy use is the third step in the ongoing energy-efficient operation process.

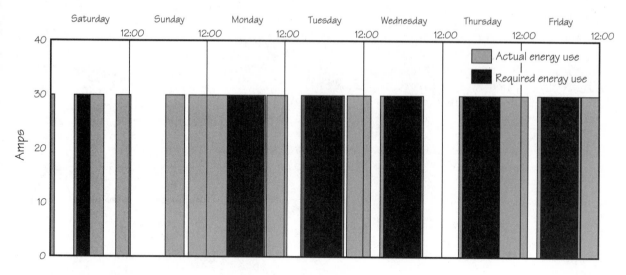

Figure 8-15. The dark-shaded area represents the required energy use profile for air handler fans during a seven-day period.

The team members were unable to calculate precisely the excess cooling energy represented by the excess operating hours. Noting that the excess cooling hours were occurring during nighttime hours when the cooling load was reduced, they felt safe in assuming that the cooling energy would be reduced by approximately 50 percent if the rooftop unit operated 88 percent fewer hours per week.

Performing detailed calculations to determine the excess energy used caused by the failed economizer control and by the excessively low supply air temperature was beyond the technical capabilities of the energy team. However, after referring to Figure 8-13, the group felt comfortable estimating that these malfunctions were adding approximately 20 percent to their cooling costs.

### Identify Strategies and Take Action

Based on the information thus far collected, the energy management team members began listing actions they might take to improve operating efficiency. The following actions were suggested:

- The team decided that the greatest energy savings potential could be realized by operating the air handler on the required schedule. The technician who programs the air handler controller was asked to set the controller to the agreed-upon schedule.

- The mechanical maintenance staff investigated the override control mechanism and discovered that the thermostat that signals the air handler to operate during unoccupied hours had been inadvertently set at 75°F instead of the expected 85°F. It was reset at 85°F.

Figure 8-16. Air handlers in this building operated 60 percent more hours than expected due to an undetected malfunction of the control system.

- It was noticed that the room in which the thermostat is located is smaller than it was when the building was constructed, partly because of added partitioning. In addition, the space now contains a copier and a number of vending machines, the heat from which causes the space temperature to rise shortly after the air-handling unit goes off. This controlling thermostat was relocated to a more representative space.

- Technicians were called to investigate the mixed air "economizer" control function and to calibrate the supply air temperature sensor.

- The duct pressure sensor, which controls the supply fan inlet vanes, was located and found to be malfunctioning. This equipment was repaired in order to restore the fan's ability to maintain a constant duct static pressure and to vary the quantity of air in response to the position of the variable-air-volume boxes.

After these repairs were completed, all of the previous measurements were repeated for a period of seven consecutive days to determine whether or not the actual operation now matched the required operation. Some minor malfunctions persisted but were eliminated after subsequent repair.

This experience convinced the energy management team of the high probability of energy-wasting malfunctions going undetected unless the group periodically and routinely measured the actual performance of the significant indicators of energy performance. Based on this experience, the team decided that it would be cost-effective to repeat the air handler measurement four times a year in order to ensure that the air handlers were using only as much energy as necessary to perform their intended function.

# CHAPTER 9

# Adapting the Process to Various Facility Types

The previous chapters of this book describe the efficient operation process and illustrate its application to a lighting system and an air-handling system. While the methods vary slightly, both examples illustrate a basic process that can be adapted to all energy consuming devices in any facility.

Most facilities have heating, ventilation and air conditioning (HVAC) systems, with components such as boilers, chillers, cooling towers, steam distribution systems, air handlers, heat pumps and exhaust systems. All of these systems have the potential to waste energy through inefficient operation. In addition, overhead lighting, office equipment, task lighting and kitchen equipment often waste enough energy dollars to justify efforts to improve their operating efficiency. It is the energy manager's job to adapt this process to their facility's unique set of energy consumers.

In some facilities, the energy manager must also adapt the process to the organizational structure of the occupants. In non-owner-occupied facilities, for example, the organization of the occupant groups affects where the process should be focused and where the most savings can be achieved. The first section of this chapter illustrates how the efficient operation process should be adapted to account for the structure of institutional facilities. The second section shows how it can be applied to improving the energy-efficiency of industrial facilities and processes.

## APPLICATION TO INSTITUTIONAL FACILITIES

The energy-efficient operation process attempts to involve all the people whose attitudes, needs and behavior influence the operation of the significant energy-consuming devices. This involvement can range from the workers who maintain boilers to the office staff who operate office equipment. In owner-occupied facilities, where all of these people answer to the same management structure, it is possible to ensure their participation and influence their behavior.

However, in institutional facilities that house numerous occupant groups, there often is no management structure with authority over everyone. Examples include colleges, universities, hospitals and most government facilities. In these facilities the energy manager cannot insist on the involvement of all the people who affect energy use, and must recognize that the operation of some equipment is outside of their control. The institutional energy manager should begin by listing the significant energy-consuming devices (as described in Chapter 3), and then subdivide that list into those items over which they have control and those items over which they have no control.

For example, in a university laboratory building, the facilities department typically has little authority to insist on the cooperation of the academic heads. They in turn may have limited ability to influence the attitudes of faculty, and the faculty may have even less ability to modify the behavior of the students in matters pertaining to energy use. In this case, the facility manager would be well advised to begin with the equipment or the features of equipment that they can control directly.

In a laboratory building, the hours when people are in the building—and, therefore, the hours when heating, ventilating and air conditioning are needed—may be

Figure 9-1. The energy-efficient operation process can be effectively applied to institutional facilities.

outside of the facility department's control. However, the department can ensure that the boilers, chillers and air handlers operate efficiently whenever they are in use. The operation of laboratory hoods and laboratory equipment may be determined by faculty and students, but facilities personnel may be able to coordinate with the custodial or security staffs to ensure that lighting and other equipment are turned off when the building is unoccupied. Over time, the facility department could attempt to build communication with administration and faculty and to gradually involve them in the process of efficiently operating the equipment they control.

Hospitals are another example of facilities occupied by multiple groups. Doctors, nurses, laboratory staff and administrative staff tend to operate somewhat independently, and there is seldom an overall management structure that could facilitate the formation of energy teams representing all occupant groups. The hospital energy manager should begin by implementing the efficient operation process on those components of the heating and cooling systems that are directly controlled by the facilities staff.

In institutional facilities, it is sometimes possible to establish a temporary energy team to deal with a specific issue. This point is illustrated by a hospital that formed an energy team to deal with the energy costs associated with operating rooms. The facility manager had observed that three operating rooms were kept in fully occupied mode at all times, despite the fact that only one was typically used for emergency surgeries on nights and weekends. The facility manager met with the surgeons and the emergency room management to verify that three operating rooms had to be in readiness at all times. He had done sufficient homework to determine that $20,000 per year could be saved for each room that could be turned off during the hours when surgeries are usually not scheduled.

The team determined that three rooms were kept in readiness based on the assumption that it would take four or five hours for a room in the unoccupied mode to return to the required environmental conditions. The group decided to measure the room recovery rate and discovered that conditions could be recovered in 45 minutes. Based on this measured information, the surgical staff felt comfortable in keeping just two operating rooms in readiness, thus yielding significant energy and cost savings.

While the management structure in institutional facilities may inhibit the ability to ensure the efficient operation of all energy-consuming systems, the opportunities to save energy in the systems that are under the control of the facility manager are typically attractive enough to justify the effort to do so.

The suggestions made above also apply to adapting the energy efficient operation process to multi-tenant office and commercial buildings, as well as multi-tenant residential structures.

## ADAPTING THE PROCESS TO INDUSTRIAL FACILITIES

The energy-efficient operation process described in the previous chapters can be applied to industrial settings with little special adaptation. The energy manager should view each process as just another energy-consuming system, and each component as just another energy-consuming device. The three start-up activities in this book can be applied with little change and the ongoing steps can be applied without adaptation. The following example, drawn from the author's personal experience, illustrates how the methods described in this book can result in substantial savings in industrial applications.

An energy manager working in an industrial facility was asked to identify opportunities to reduce the plant's $1,276,000 annual utility bill. The manager began by

Figure 9-2. The efficient operation process can reduce the energy consumed by industrial processes as well as for buildings of all types.

listing the major categories of energy consumers and by doing a rough allocation of the annual energy dollars to the largest energy users (see Figure 9-3). His analysis indicated that the largest contributor to energy cost was fuels consumed in heating at the paint lines (water heating at washers and heating at bake ovens), and the fifth-largest item was electricity consumed by paint line fans and pumps. In total, the paint line consumed $653,000 a year, which accounted for just over 50 percent of the total cost of energy for the facility. The energy manager called together a small team to review the paint line operations and to determine whether there were any opportunities to reduce paint line energy costs. The following dialogue is a simulation of the content of their meetings.

**Energy Manager:** I've called you together because I want to review the energy consumption of our paint lines. As you can see from Figure 9-3, the paint lines consume over $650,000 per year in energy and are our single largest area of energy cost. I have allocated the total paint line cost to the five major components, as you can see in Figure 9-4. Our objective here is to review each component to either verify that it is operating as efficiently as it can or identify opportunities to improve its efficiency. Based on my allocation, it seems reasonable to start with the largest items and work towards the smallest, and therefore we should start with the bake ovens. Mr. Painting Engineer, what are the significant variables that affect energy costs in the bake ovens?

**Painting Engineer:** The ovens use direct-fired gas burners to bake the paint. Actually, we don't bake the paint directly, but we do heat air, which then dries the paint.

**Paint Line Manager:** I suppose the amount of air we heat has to do with how much air we exhaust out of the ovens. Isn't that right?

**Painting Engineer:** Yes, that's right. We need to exhaust air continuously from the ovens to prevent a build-up of volatiles that could cause an explosion.

Figure 9-3. Energy cost allocation for an industrial plant.

| Item | Annual Cost |
|------|-------------|
| Air handling fans | $10,700 |
| Exhaust fans | $17,200 |
| Lighting | $51,500 |
| Make-up air unit fans | $23,600 |
| Production equipment motor | $175,000 |
| **Paint line fans and pumps** | **$108,900** |
| Air compressors | $40,800 |
| Space heating | $113,080 |
| Make-up air heating | $214,260 |
| **Paint line heating** | **$543,900** |
| Total | $1,275,290 |

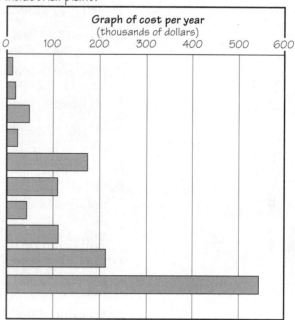

Figure 9-4. Energy cost allocation for the paint line components.

| Item | Annual Cost |
|------|-------------|
| Dry spray booth | $26,000 |
| Wet spray booth | $39,500 |
| Dry ovens | $52,500 |
| Washers | $163,200 |
| **Bake ovens** | **$371,600** |
| Total | $652,800 |

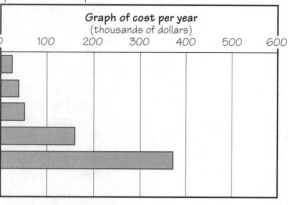

**Paint Line Manager**: How much air do we exhaust?

**Painting Engineer**: I think we exhaust about 30,000 cfm.

**Paint Line Manager**: Has that amount been changed at all in the last two years?

**Production Maintenance**: I've been here nine years and as far as I know, we've had the same exhaust system exhausting the same quantity of air all that time.

**Paint Line Manager**: Did we make any changes when we switched to powdered paint two years ago?

**Production Maintenance**: I'm sure we didn't.

**Painting Engineer**: Powdered paint has almost no volatiles, and I'm sure that quantity of exhaust could be reduced at least 75%. How much do you suppose that would save?

**Energy Manager**: I would have to calculate it, but I guess it would be in the range of $40,000 to $50,000 per year.

**Paint Line Manager**: I would like Painting Engineer to work with Production Maintenance to reduce the exhaust as much as possible while still maintaining adequate ventilation for safety. Be sure to do enough measurements of volatiles to be certain that we are not creating any risk.

**Energy Manager**: What other factors contribute to the energy consumed by the bake ovens?

**Painting Engineer**: The oven temperature is significant but I've recently worked through that with our paint chemist and we've confirmed that we need to maintain 480° in the oven. Another variable, of course, is the hours that the ovens operate.

**Energy Manager**: What time do the ovens go on and off?

**Production Maintenance**: We have the first shift production maintenance person start the ovens when he first comes in at 4:30 a.m.

**Energy Manager**: Why do we start them at 4:30 a.m.?

**Production Maintenance**: So they will be up to temperature when the plant opens at 8:00 a.m.

**Energy Manager**: Let's verify how long it takes for the ovens to get up to temperature.

**Production Maintenance**: Why don't you datalog the oven temperatures during start-up for the next week and report at our next meeting?

*(Meeting adjourned and reconvened two weeks later).*

**Energy Manager**: When we left off, we were talking about the necessary operating hours of the ovens. Production Maintenance, did you find out how long it takes for the ovens to come up to temperature?

**Production Maintenance**: Yes, I pretty well confirmed that 30 minutes is more than enough to bring the ovens up to temperature.

Figure 9-5. Industrial air compressors are major consumers of electricity. The application of the energy-efficient operation process is necessary to avoid significant energy waste.

**Painting Engineer**: It looks like we could start the ovens at 7:30 a.m. instead of 4:30 a.m. That's three hours of operating savings per day, or 15 hours per week.

**Paint Line Manager**: We could start the ovens at 7:30 a.m. to have them up to temperature by 8:00 a.m. when the plant opens. The paint line actually starts at 8:00 a.m., but the products have to be washed, dried and painted before they arrive at the bake ovens. I don't think the first product arrives at the bake oven until about 9:00 a.m., so I think we could delay starting the ovens until 8:30 a.m.

**Energy Manager**: I want to thank you for your participation in this process. What we have done here is review how we actually operate the bake ovens and then ask ourselves how we really need to operate them. We discovered a significant savings opportunity in the difference between actual and required operation. We found that we could reduce the exhaust quantity by 75 percent, which equals a 75 percent reduction in air heating. We also shortened the operating hours by about 25 percent. This has been a very fruitful process. At our next meeting, we will begin reviewing the operation of the washers.

In this actual example of the efficient operation process, the energy manager and his paint line energy team succeeded in reducing the plant energy costs by $67,000 per year by making the oven use only as much energy as necessary to perform its intended function. It should be noted that the savings cost almost nothing to achieve. This example illustrates the benefits of applying the basic methods described in this book to energy-consuming industrial processes.

## SUMMARY

The first chapters of this book introduce the general concepts of energy-efficient operation and subsequent chapters illustrate these concepts in considerable detail.

When involved in the details of the process, it is important to keep in mind the major themes:

- Many energy-consuming devices in buildings and in industrial processes use more energy than necessary to perform their intended functions.

- This inefficient operation can waste 10 to 25 percent of all energy purchased.

- Inefficient operation is not detectable by typical operating and maintenance practices.

- A new process must be added to current practices to achieve and sustain operating efficiency.

- This energy-efficient operation process should be based on activities common to all management processes. These activities are:

    A. Measure actual performance.

    B. Compare to required performance.

    C. Take action when actual performance does not match required performance.

- The facilitation of this energy-efficient operation process should be an essential component of the energy manager's job.

It is the author's sincere hope that the development of these themes and the description of the tasks in this book will provide readers with a conceptual base upon which to build their own energy-efficient operation process. The basics of this process can be applied anywhere—the energy manager's job is to adapt it to their facility's unique characteristics and potential for savings.

The rewards for achieving and sustaining operating efficiency are great. In addition to significant dollar savings, the energy manager can play a role in reducing needless waste of natural resources, help stem the flow of energy dollars out of their state and country, and reduce the environmental degradation associated with energy production and use.

# APPENDIX A

# Estimating the Annual Cost to Operate Electrical Devices

This appendix describes simplified methods for estimating the annual energy dollars consumed by electrical devices and systems typically found in buildings. The purpose of these estimates is to determine the relative magnitude of each energy user, thereby helping the energy manager establish priorities. At this stage, the goal is to determine whether a particular item's annual operation costs $300 or $3,000. Does it consume 2 percent of the energy budget or 20 percent? The estimating procedures described in this appendix are sufficiently precise to achieve these objectives, yet they are simple enough to be performed by people who have minimal technical background.

The experienced energy manager will recognize two areas of simplification that he or she may wish to make more precise. The first is the use of an electrical unit cost that represents the blend of demand charges (kW) and kilowatt hour (kWh) charges. Appendix C provides a procedure for allocating these costs separately. The second area concerns the absence of power factor in the equations to calculate kilowatt hours. This potential problem has been accommodated in the factor used to convert motor horsepower to kilowatts. People who are knowledgeable about power factor can add a factor in the other equations. However, the novice energy manager can accept these simplifications and still achieve sufficient accuracy for the purposes of these estimates.

The electrical estimating process begins with the creation of a form for summarizing the results of all the individual estimates. The form shown in Figure A-1 is recommended and is used in the examples throughout this book. To begin, enter the significant electrical consumers listed in Chapter 3 (see Figure 3-7 on page 34) under Column C. Note that the list of items has been subdivided into constant (non-weather-variable) and weather-variable consumers of electricity. Also note that the total known annual electrical consumption determined in Chapter 4 (see Figure 4-3 on page 53) has been entered on the form at the bottom of Column D. The objective of these estimates is to allocate that known total to the various consumers.

**ELECTRICAL ENERGY USE**

Item A: $0.053 per kWh

| B | C | D | E | F |
|---|---|---|---|---|
| | Item | Estimated annual kWh | Annual cost | Percent of total cost |
| Constant electrical uses | E-1. Lighting | | | |
| | E-2. Air handling fans | | | |
| | E-3. Office equipment | | | |
| | E-4. Exhaust fans | | | |
| | E-5. Elevators | | | |
| | E-6. | | | |
| | E-7. Miscellaneous | | | |
| | E-8. Subtotals | | | |
| Weather-variable electrical uses | E-9. Air conditioning | | | |
| | E-10. | | | |
| | E-11. Subtotals | | | |
| | E-12. Electric totals | 858,560 | $45,081 | |

Figure A-1. Allocation of annual electrical energy cost—total electrical use and cost are known.

The procedures for estimating the annual energy costs are arranged in the following order:

*Constant (non-weather-variable) electrical users:*

- Lighting
- Constant rate electrical motors
- Variable rate electrical motors
- Two-speed motors
- Office equipment
- Electrical water heaters
- Miscellaneous equipment

*Weather-variable electrical users:*

- Electrical cooling
- Electrical heating
- Electric heat pumps

## ESTIMATING CONSTANT ELECTRICAL CONSUMPTION

### Lighting

Lighting is a visible and often very significant energy use in nonresidential buildings. General lighting usually consists of fluorescent fixtures, and other types of lighting are used for task lighting, outdoor lighting or creating special design effects. This appendix presents two methods for making a quick estimate of energy consumption for lighting.

### Estimating Lighting Use—Takeoff Method

To estimate energy use for fluorescent light fixtures, follow these steps:

1. Determine the watts for each lamp (printed on the lamps).

> Watts is the product of amps times volts (e.g., a computer drawing 1.2 amps from a 120-volt receptacle circuit is consuming 1.2 x 120 = 144 watts).
>
> Electricity is expressed (and billed) in kilowatts (kW) and kilowatt hours (kWh). Therefore, always divide calculated watts by 1,000 to get kW and kWh.

## Example of the Lighting Takeoff Method:

A review of the example building and its electrical lighting drawings shows that the vast majority of the building's overhead lighting is provided by a repeating pattern of 2- x 2-foot-square fluorescent fixtures, each with two 34-watt lamps.

(2 lamps x 34 watts) + 10% for ballast = 74.8 watts per fixture

There are approximately 150 fixtures on each of the 4 floors, for a total of 599 fixtures.

$$\text{Total building lighting kW} = \frac{599 \text{ fixtures} \times 74.8 \text{ watts}}{1000} = 44.8 \text{ kW}$$

Calculate annual kWh by multiplying kW by the operating schedule information (see Figure 4-7 on page 58) as follows:

44.8 kW x 10% x 168 hrs/wk x 52 wks/yr = 39,137 kWh/yr

44.8 kW x 90% x 75 hrs/wk x 50 wks/yr = 151,200 kWh/yr

44.8 kW x 30% x 6.5 hrs/wk x 50 wks/yr = <u>4,368 kWh/yr</u>
194,705 kWh/yr

Enter this estimate of annual overhead lighting electrical usage on Line E-1—Column D of Figure A-3.

2. Multiply this wattage by the number of lamps in each fixture and add 10 percent for the lighting ballast.

3. Multiply this watts per fixture total by the approximate fixture count to determining the total watts for the building (divide by 1,000 to convert to kilowatts).

4. Multiply the total kilowatts for the building by the operating schedule information recorded on Figure 4-7 to arrive at an estimate of kilowatt hours per year for lighting.

Repeat this procedure for each group of light fixtures that have different wattage, number of lamps per fixture, or operating schedule. Similarly, follow this procedure for incandescent task lights. (Note: Because incandescent lights do not have ballasts, it is not necessary to add 10 percent.) Finally, total all the lighting use in the building.

## Estimating Lighting Use—Measurement Method

In buildings where entire electrical panels are dedicated to lighting, it is possible to measure the amperage at these locations during typical operating conditions and use these measurements to make an estimate of annual consumption. Two basic types of power are supplied for lighting circuits—single phase and three phase. Methods to measure and calculate each are described below.

### Single-Phase Lighting Panels

The kilowatts of electrical consumption for a lighting panel served by a single feeder plus ground (single phase) can be determined by the following steps:

1. Measure the amps at the lighting panel feeder with an ammeter.

2. Multiply the amps by the voltage to calculate watts (divide by 1,000 to convert to kilowatts).

**Example of Lighting Measurement Method—Single-Phase Power**

The feeder to a 120-volt panel serving lighting measures 47.8 amps. The kilowatts are calculated as follows:

47.8 amps x 120 volts = 5736 watts = 5.7 kW

Calculate the annual kWh by multiplying kW by the estimated hours of operation per year.

---

**Example of Lighting Measurement Methods—Three-Phase Power**

The three wires into a 277/480-volt three-phase lighting panel measure 12.2 amps , 18.6 amps and 15.3 amps, respectively.

The *sum of three phases method* calculation is as follows:

(12.2+18.6+15.3) x 277 volts = 12,770 watts = 12.8 kW

The *average of three phases method* calculation is as follows:

$$\frac{(12.2+18.6+15.3)}{3} \times 480 \text{ volts} \times 1.732 = 12,775 \text{ watts} = 12.8 \text{ kW}$$

Note that these two methods yield the same result. Calculate the annual kWh by multiplying kW by the estimated hours of operation per year.

3. Multiply the total kilowatts by the operating schedule information (see Figure 4-7 on page 58) to arrive at an estimate of kilowatt hours per year for lighting from the location being measured.

Repeat this procedure for each lighting panel location that is measured. Total the results to determine the energy for all single-phase lighting in the building.

### Three-Phase Lighting Panels

The kilowatts of electricity consumed by lighting panels served by three feeders (three phase) can be determined by the following steps. This is referred to as the *sum of three phases method*:

1. Measure the amps at each feeder entering the lighting panel with an ammeter.

2. Sum the amps for all three feeders.

3. Multiply this sum by the phase-to-ground voltage (usually 120 volts or 277 volts).

4. Divide by 1,000 to convert to kilowatts.

An alternative calculation method can also be used for three-phase power. This is referred to as the *average of three phases method:*

1. Measure the amps at each feeder entering the lighting panel with an ammeter.

2. Average the amps for all three feeders.

3. Multiply this average by the phase-to-phase voltage (usually 208 volts or 480 volts).

4. Multiply this product by 1.732 (the square root of 3).

5. Divide by 1,000 to convert to kilowatts.

### Constant Rate Electric Motors

Most electric motors used in buildings operate at a constant speed and consume electricity at a more or less constant rate whenever they are operating. Examples include motors that drive exhaust fans, pumps, heat pump fans and constant volume air handler fans.

The following methods can be used to estimate the annual electrical consumption of electric motors that operate at a constant rate.

### Estimating Constant Rate Electric Motor Use— Takeoff Method

To estimate energy use for a constant rate electric motor, follow these steps:

1. Determine the horsepower (hp) for each motor (printed on the nameplate of the motor).

2. Multiply this horsepower by 0.55 kW per hp to obtain the kilowatts of electricity consumed by the motor.

3. Multiply the kilowatts for the motor by the operating schedule information (see Figure 4-7 on page 58) to arrive at an estimate of kilowatt hours per year for the motor.

Repeat this procedure for each motor or group of similar motors, then total all the constant speed motor use in the building.

### Estimating Constant Rate Electric Motor Use— Measurement Method

A more accurate method to determine the kW of electricity consumed by a constant rate motor is to measure the actual amps of electricity drawn by the motor while in operation. A clamp-on ammeter can be used to measure the amps carried by the single line of supply in a single-phase motor or in all three lines of supply in a three-phase motor. These measured amps can then be used to calculate the actual kilowatts of the motor.

> The factor 0.55 is derived from actual amp measurements taken on hundreds of motors typically found in buildings. The factor accounts for part load characteristics and power factor, resulting in a rule of thumb that provides a rough estimate of a motor's energy use as seen by the electric meter.

## Example of the Takeoff Method for Constant Rate Motors:

This example illustrates how to determine the electrical use of our example building's toilet exhaust fans. The inventory of equipment showed one exhaust fan serving the men's toilet rooms and one serving the women's toilet rooms, at 1 horsepower each, for a total of 2 horsepower.

2 hp x .55 kW per hp = 1.1 kW

The schedule of operation (see Figure 4-7 on page 58) indicates that these exhaust fans operate 168 hours per week, 52 weeks per year.

1.1 kW x 168 hrs per wk x 52 wks per yr = 9,610 kWh per yr

Enter this annual usage number on Line E-4—Column D of Figure A-3.

## Example of the Measurement Method for Constant Rate Motors—Single-Phase Power

The single 120-volt conductor to a constant speed motor measures 7.8 amps. The kilowatts are calculated as follows:

7.8 amps x 120 volts = 936 watts = .94 kW

Calculate the annual kilowatt hours by multiplying kilowatts by the estimated hours of operation per year.

*Single Phase Constant Rate Electric Motors*

The kilowatts of electrical consumption for motors served by a single source of current (single phase) can be determined by the following steps:

1. Measure the amps at the conductor to the motor with an ammeter.

2. Multiply the amps by the voltage to calculate watts (divide by 1,000 to convert to kilowatts).

3. Multiply the total kilowatts by the operating schedule information (see Figure 4-7 on page 58) to arrive at an estimate of kilowatt hours per year for the motor being measured.

Repeat this procedure for each motor that is measured and total the results to determine the energy for all single-phase motor use in the building.

*Three-Phase Constant Rate Electric Motors*

The kilowatts of electricity consumed by a motor served by three conductors (three phase) can be determined by the following steps. This is referred to as the *sum of three phases method*:

1. Using an ammeter, measure the amps at all three conductors for a particular motor.

2. Sum the amps for all three phases.

3. Multiply this sum by the phase to ground voltage (usually 120 volts or 277 volts).

4. Divide by 1,000 to convert to kilowatts.

An alternative calculation method can also be used for three-phase power. This is referred to as the *average of three phases method:*

1. Using an ammeter, measure the amps at all three conductors for a particular motor.

2. Average the amps for all three phases.

3. Multiply this average by the phase-to-phase voltage (usually 208 volts or 480 volts).

## Example of the Measurement Method for Constant Rate Motors—Three-Phase Power

Our example building has two elevators—one with a 25 hp/three-phase motor and the other with a 30 hp/three-phase motor—and each operates at 277/480 volts.

The operating current draw for the three phases of the 25-hp motor was measured at 22, 24 and 23 amps. Using the *sum of three phases* method, the first elevator motor's kilowatts are calculated as follows:

$(22 + 24 + 23) \times 277$ volts = 19,113 watts = 19.1 kW

While it is true that the amp draw on an elevator motor will vary with the number of people in the elevator, a reasonable approximation of the annual electrical use can be achieved by assuming a constant amp draw.

The three phases of the 30-hp motor measured 26, 28 and 28 amps. Using the *sum of three phases* method again, the second elevator motor's kilowatts are calculated as follows:

$(26 + 28 + 28) \times 277$ volts = 22,714 watts = 22.7 kW

The total operating kilowatts for both elevator motors is:

19.1 kW + 22.7 kW = 41.8 kW

The schedule of use (see Figure 4-7 on page 58) indicates that the elevators are in motion 10 hours per week, 50 weeks per year. The annual kilowatt hours for the elevator motors can then be estimated as follows:

41.8 kW x 10 hrs per wk x 50 wks per yr = 20,900 kWh per yr

Enter this annual usage on Line E-5—Column D in Figure A-3.

4. Multiply this product by 1.732 (square root of 3).

5. Divide by 1,000 to convert to kilowatts.

## Variable-Rate Electrical Motors

Some electrical motors vary in speed and/or vary in their rate of electricity consumption in response to a varying load on the device the motor drives. One example is motors equipped with variable-speed drives. These can be recognized by the presence of variable-speed drive equipment on the wiring path between the motor and the electrical panel that serves it. Examples include variable-speed pumps and variable-speed air-handling unit fans.

A second category is motors that vary their rate of electrical consumption in response to varying loads. Examples are central chilling system compressors, as well as larger rooftop cooling units and heat pumps. Also included in this category are motors that drive variable-output pumps or fans. The most common example of this type of motor is in variable-volume air systems, where the output of the fans is varied by inlet vanes or outlet dampers.

The final category of variable-rate motors are those specifically designed to operate at two speeds. These are occasionally found on fans or pumps that need to operate at "high/low" speeds. Two-speed motors can be recognized by examining their nameplate data.

The general approach to estimating the annual electrical consumption of all variable rate motors is to make an approximation of the *average* kilowatts drawn by the motor when it is operating and then multiply this number by the annual operating hours. It should be noted that the estimates of energy consumption performed at this stage in the process can be very approximate, yet still perform their intended function of showing the relative magnitude of energy consumed by the various energy input sites. In Chapter 6, actual measurements of energy use are performed; this information can be used to refine and edit the approximations done at this stage.

The two examples of estimating electrical use of

variable speed motors given here are both takeoff methods—one for variable-speed motors and one for two-speed motors. The measurement method of reading amps, calculating kilowatts and multiplying by operating hours is possible for variable-speed motors. However, it is recommended that a number of amp readings be taken at various times in order to approximate the average operating amps.

## Estimating Electrical Use of Motors with Variable-Speed Drives—Takeoff Method

To estimate energy use for a motor equipped with variable-speed drive, follow these steps:

1. Determine the horsepower (hp) for each motor (printed on the nameplate of the motor).

2. Multiply this horsepower by 0.55 kW per hp to obtain the kilowatts of electricity consumed by the motor when it is running at full capacity.

3. Estimate the average output of the pump or fan during its hours of operation. In the case of pumps, estimate the average percent of full capacity gallons per minute (gpm); in the case of fans, estimate the average percent of full capacity cubic feet per minute (cfm) of air. If no information is available upon which to base this estimate, begin with an estimate of 70 to 80 percent and refine this number in the future when better information is available.

4. Using the chart in Figure A-2, find the kilowatt input factor (from the second column) that corresponds to the estimated average percent device output determined in the previous step.

5. Multiply the kilowatts of the motor at full capacity (from Step 2) by the kilowatt input factor (from Step 4) to determine the actual average kilowatts.

6. Multiply the kilowatts for the motor (from Step 5) by the operating schedule information (see Figure 4-7 on page 58) to arrive at an estimate of kilowatt hours per year for the motor.

Figure A-2. Input versus output data for fans and pumps with variable-speed drives.

| Average percent of full load | |
|---|---|
| Device output | KW input |
| 100% | 1.00 |
| 90% | 0.73 |
| 80% | 0.51 |
| 70% | 0.22 |
| 50% | 0.06 |
| 30% | 0.03 |

## Example of Takeoff Method for Variable-Speed Motors:

This example shows how to determine the electrical use of an air handler with a variable-speed drive and rated at 25 horsepower.

25 hp x 0.55 kW per hp  = 13.75 kW (at full load)

The average device output is estimated at 80 percent. The corresponding kilowatt input factor found in Figure A-2 is 0.51 (or 51 percent).

13.75 kW x 0.51 = 7.01 kW (at 80 percent load)

This is the average operating kilowatts. The schedule of operation indicates that this fan operates 78 hours per week, 52 weeks per year.

7.01 kW x 78 hrs per wk x 52 wks per yr = 28,433 kWh per yr

## Example of Takeoff Method for Two-Speed Motors:

This example shows how to determine the electrical use of a continuously operating two-speed fan motor. The fan is rated at 4 horsepower.

4 hp x 0.55 kW per hp  = 2.2 kW (at high speed)

2.2 kW x 0.50 = 1.1 kW (at low speed)

It is estimated that the fan runs 60 percent of the time at low speed and 40 percent at high speed.

(2.2 kW x 0.40) + (1.1 kW x 0.60) = 1.54 kW

This is the average operating kilowatts. The fans operate 168 hours per week, 52 weeks per year.

1.54 kW x 168 hrs per wk x 52 wks per yr = 13,453 kWh per yr

Repeat this procedure for each motor or group of similar motors, then total all the motors in the building with variable-speed drives.

## Estimating Two-Speed Electric Motor Use— Takeoff Method

The annual kilowatt hours for two-speed motors can be quickly estimated, based on the assumption that the kilowatt input for the low-speed operation is 50 percent of the kilowatt input for the high-speed operation. To estimate energy use for a two-speed electric motor, follow these steps:

1. Determine the horsepower (hp) for each motor (printed on the nameplate of the motor).

2. Multiply this horsepower by 0.55 kW per hp to obtain the kilowatts of electricity consumed by the motor when it is running at high speed.

3. Multiply the kilowatt input for the motor at high speed (from Step 2) by 0.50 (or 50 percent) to determine the kilowatt input for the motor at low speed.

4. Estimate the percent of operating time at high speed and at low speed and use those percentages in the following formula to calculate the average kilowatts.

   (high speed kW x % of time at high speed)

   + (low speed kW x % of time at low speed) = average kW

5. Multiply the average kilowatts for the motor (from Step 4) by the operating schedule information recorded on Figure 4-7 on page 58 to arrive at an estimate of kilowatt hours per year for the motor.

This method can also be used for two-stage chilling compressors on central chillers, rooftop units and heat pumps.

## Estimating Variable-Rate Electric Motor Use—Measurement Method

The annual kilowatt hours for motors of variable load can be estimated based on measured amp readings taken at various times and averaged to represent the typical current draw. The kilowatts of electricity consumed by a variable-speed motor served by three conductors (three phase) can be determined by the following steps:

1. Using an ammeter, measure the amps at all three conductors for a particular motor.

2. Sum the amps for all three phases.

3. Repeat Steps 1 and 2 several times to get a variety of readings, and determine the average of the readings taken.

4. Multiply this average by the phase-to-ground voltage (usually 120 volts or 277 volts).

5. Divide by 1,000 to convert to kilowatts.

## Office Equipment

The amount of energy consumed by computers, printers, copiers, etc., has grown steadily in recent years and represents an ever-increasing portion of office building energy use and cost. A significant contributor to this use is the common finding that 25 to 50 percent of office equipment operates continuously on days, nights and weekends. One important goal for any office building energy efficiency program is to eliminate any unnecessary (i.e., unoccupied hour) operation of office equipment.

A simple method for estimating the electrical energy consumed by office equipment is to multiply the office area by a watts-per-square-foot factor representative of office spaces. Equipment in typical offices use between 0.5 and 1.0 watts per square foot. Select a number in this range, depending upon the density of computers, printers, copiers, etc.; then multiply this factor by the assumed hours of operation to estimate the kilowatt hours per year.

## Example of Measurement Method for Variable Speed Motors

Our example building has two air handlers, each equipped with one 25-horsepower supply fan and one 20-horsepower return fan. Each fan has a 277/480-volt supply fan motor (three phase) on a variable air volume system. The fan load is varied by variable inlet vanes. The amps were measured at each of the three conductors to this three-phase motor and the three readings were added together. These measurements, taken at four different times during a typical day, yielded an average value of 54.6 amps.

The average sum of the three phases is multiplied by the phase-to-ground voltage to determine average kilowatts as follows:

54.6 amps x 277 volts = 15,124 watts = 15.1 kW

This is the average operating kilowatts. The schedule of operation indicates that this fan operates 78 hours per week, 52 weeks per year.

15.1 kW x 78 hrs per week x 52 wks per year = 61,245 kWh per year.

This calculation is repeated for each of the four fans in the building. The resulting estimates are:

| | | |
|---|---|---|
| Supply fan no. 1 | 61,245 | kWh/yr |
| Return fan no. 1 | 51,855 | kWh/yr |
| Supply fan no. 2 | 62,350 | kWh/yr |
| Return fan no. 2 | 49,940 | kWh/yr |
| Total | 225,390 | kWh/yr |

Enter this total on Line E-2 of Column D of Figure A-3.

A more accurate method is to inventory the nameplate power use for the equipment found in a representative sample area of office space (for example, 1,000 square feet) and calculate a watts-per-square-foot factor appropriate for the space (multiply nameplate power use by .75 to account for the fact that equipment seldom draws full nameplate power).

The most reliable method for approximating office equipment annual electrical use is to measure the amp flow at panels serving equipment loads and then convert those amps to kilowatts by the methods described below.

### Estimating Office Equipment Use— Measurement Method

In buildings where entire electrical panels are dedicated to office equipment, it is possible to measure the amperage at these locations during typical operating conditions and then make an estimate of annual consumption. There are two basic types of power supplied for these circuits: single phase and three phase. Methods to measure and calculate each are described below.

*Single-Phase Power for Office Equipment*

The kilowatts of electrical consumption for office equipment served by a single feeder plus ground (single phase) can be determined by the following steps:

1. Measure the amps at the electric panel with an ammeter.

2. Multiply the amps by the voltage to calculate watts (divide by 1,000 to convert to kilowatts).

3. Multiply the total kilowatts by the operating schedule information (see Figure 4-7 on page 58) to arrive at an estimate of kilowatt hours per year for office equipment in the location being measured.

Repeat this procedure for each electrical panel location that is measured and total the results to deter-

**Example of Measurement Method—
Single-Phase Power**

The feeder to a 120-volt panel serving office equipment measures 7.8 amps. The kilowatts are calculated as follows:

7.8 amps x 120 volts = 936 watts = 0.94 kW

mine the energy for all office equipment on single-phase power in the building.

*Three-Phase Power for Office Equipment*

The kilowatts of electricity consumed by office equipment panels served by three feeders simultaneously (three phase) can be determined by the following steps. This is referred to as the *sum of three phases method*:

1. Measure the amps at each feeder entering the electric panel with an ammeter.

2. Sum the amps for all three feeders.

3. Multiply this sum by the phase to ground voltage (usually 120 volts or 277 volts).

4. Divide by 1,000 to convert to kilowatts.

An alternative calculation method can also be used for three-phase power. This is referred to as the *average of three phases method*:

1. Measure the amps at each feeder entering the lighting panel with an ammeter.

2. Average the amps for all three feeders.

3. Multiply this average by the phase to phase voltage (usually 208 volts or 480 volts).

4. Multiply this product by 1.732.

5. Divide by 1,000 to convert to kilowatts.

## Example of Measurement Method—Three-Phase Power

In our example office building, a 277/480-volt three-phase circuit feeds one transformer on each of the five levels; this transformer, in turn, provides 120/208-volt power for all office equipment on that floor (see Figure 3-12). When the typical daytime operating amps were measured at each of the three 277-volt legs serving each of the five transformers, the sum total of all 15 legs was found to be 96 amps. Using the sum of three phases method, the kilowatts were determined as follows:

96 total amps x 277 volts = 26,432 watts = 26.43 kW

Estimate the annual kilowatt hours of office equipment by multiplying the calculated kilowatts by the schedule information on Figure 4-7 (page 58) as follows:

26.43 kW x 75% x 45 hrs/wk x 50 wks/yr = 44,600 kWh/yr
26.43 kW x 25% x 168 hrs/wk x 52 wks/yr = 57,745 kWh/yr
102,345 kWh/yr

Enter this total on Line E-3—Column D in Figure A-3.

## Example of Estimating Method for Electric Water Heating

A typical office building is occupied by 450 workers and it is estimated that each person uses 1 gallon of lavatory hot water each day. The annual electrical use for water heating can be approximated as follows:

450 workers x 1 gal/day x .170 kWh/gal = 76.5 kWh per day

76.5 kWh per day x 260 work days/yr = 19,890 kWh/yr

## Electric Hot Water Heating

The annual kWh for electric hot water heating can be quickly estimated by determining the amount of hot water used daily by the occupants and multiplying that number by the electric consumption per gallon. This estimate is based on the assumption that electrical water heaters consume approximately 170 watt hours (.170 kWh) for each gallon of water heated. To estimate energy use for electric water heating, follow these steps:

1. Determine the average amount of hot water used by each occupant each day.

2. Multiply this average consumption by the total number of occupants to obtain total daily use.

3. Multiply the total daily use by 0.17 kWh per gallon to obtain total daily usage.

4. Multiply total daily usage by the number of work days during the year.

## Miscellaneous Electrical Uses

Usually there are a number of electricity-consuming devices that are too small to be itemized in this general allocation, but their aggregated energy use may account for 5 to 15 percent of the total annual electrical consumption. Examples include pneumatic control air compressors, small circulating pumps and exterior building lighting.

Account for miscellaneous electrical users by assuming they consume 10 percent of the annual total kWh. Calculate 10 percent of the total shown on Line E-12 of Figure A-3 and enter this amount on Line E-7.

Miscellaneous use = total kWh/year x 10%

Miscellaneous use = 858,560 kWh/year x 10% = 85,856 kWh

## Summary of Constant Electric Consumption

Once you have completed estimates for the various electrical energy uses presented in this task, enter them on the allocation form as shown in Figure A-3. Examples of constant electric uses are shown on Lines     E-1 through E-7.

ELECTRICAL ENERGY USE

Item A: $0.053 per kWh

Figure A-3. Allocation of annual electrical energy cost—constant electrical uses are filled in first.

| B | C | D | E | F |
|---|---|---|---|---|
| | Item | Estimated annual kWh | Annual cost | Percent of total cost |
| Constant electrical uses | E-1. Lighting | 194,700 | | |
| | E-2. Air handling fans | 225,390 | | |
| | E-3. Office equipment | 102,345 | | |
| | E-4. Exhaust fans | 9,610 | | |
| | E-5. Elevators | 20,900 | | |
| | E-6. | | | |
| | E-7. Miscellaneous | 85,856 | | |
| | E-8. Subtotals | 638,800 | $33,856 | |
| Weather-variable electrical uses | E-9. Air conditioning | | | |
| | E-10. | | | |
| | E-11. Subtotals | | | |
| | E-12. Electric totals | 858,560 | $45,081 | |

# ESTIMATING WEATHER-VARIABLE ELECTRICAL CONSUMPTION — HEATING AND COOLING SYSTEMS

Calculating the precise annual electrical use of cooling and heating systems (which vary with the weather) can be a very complex procedure requiring considerable knowledge of heating load and cooling load calculating procedures. The purpose of these energy use estimates is to gain a general knowledge of the relative proportion of the annual total that can be assigned to each major energy-consuming system; therefore, a high level of precision is not required.

The simplest approach to estimating heating and cooling energy use is to first estimate the annual use of all of the constant users and to then subtract this total from the annual energy use derived from the utility bills. This approach is illustrated for the example building below.

## Estimating Electric Cooling

In many buildings, the only weather-related system using electric energy is the space cooling (air conditioning) system. In colder climates, space cooling may only operate in the summer and heat is provided by another fuel source in winter. In warmer climates, air conditioning may be required all year, with no heating necessary.

The example building used throughout this book fits the first category—it exists in a northern climate where the weather allows the cooling system to be disabled during the winter months and heat is supplied by another fuel source.

Below are two parallel approaches that can be used to estimate the annual cooling electrical use—a calculation method and a graphical method.

### Calculation Method

If the estimates of the constant uses are relatively complete and reliable, a simple calculation procedure is

ELECTRICAL ENERGY USE

Item A: $0.053 per kWh

Figure A-4. Allocation of annual electrical energy cost—weather-related electrical uses are filled in after completing constant uses.

| B | C | D | E | F |
|---|---|---|---|---|
| | Item | Estimated annual kWh | Annual cost | Percent of total cost |
| Constant electrical uses | E-1. Lighting | 194,700 | | |
| | E-2. Air handling fans | 225,390 | | |
| | E-3. Office equipment | 102,345 | | |
| | E-4. Exhaust fans | 9,610 | | |
| | E-5. Elevators | 20,900 | | |
| | E-6. | | | |
| | E-7. Miscellaneous | 85,856 | | |
| | E-8. Subtotals | 638,800 | $33,856 | |
| Weather-variable electrical uses | E-9. Air conditioning | 219,760 | | |
| | E-10. | | | |
| | E-11. Subtotals | 219,760 | | |
| | E-12. Electric totals | 858,560 | $45,081 | |

sufficient to determine annual electric cooling use, as follows.

1. Find the total annual electric use on Line E-12, Column D of Figure A-4.

2. Find the subtotal of all constant electrical users on Line E-8, Column D of Figure A-4.

3. Subtract the constant users from the total electric use to obtain the cooling use (see formula below).

   Cooling Energy Use = Total Use – Non-Cooling Electric Use

   Cooling Energy = 858,560 – 638,800 = 219,760 kWh/yr

4. Enter this total on the allocation form, as shown on Line E-9, Column D of Figure A-4.

## Graphical Method

The graphical method is similar to the calculation method, but it adds a visual representation of the division between constant and weather-variable electrical users. The graph of the electric use from Figure 4-5 (page 56) is shown here as Figure A-5. A horizontal line is drawn on the plot, which represents a separation between the annual cooling electrical use (area above the line) and the constant electrical use (area below the line).

Using this graph, the total annual consumption for the two categories of electrical use can be depicted and calculated by following these steps:

1. Find the total annual electric use on Line E-12, Column D of Figure A-4.

2. Find the subtotal of all constant electrical users in Figure A-4, Line E-8, Column D. Determine the average Kwh per day of the constant users by dividing this subtotal by 365 days per year:

$$\frac{638,800 \ Kwh/year}{365 \ days/year} = 1,750 \ KWh/day$$

Draw a horizontal dotted line at the 1,750 kWh/day level as shown in Figure A-5.

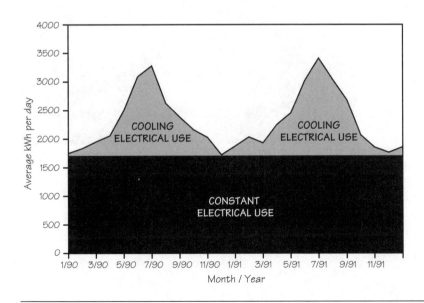

Figure A-5. Graph indicating the average daily electric use for each month of the year.

3. Subtract the constant users from the total electric use to obtain the cooling use (see formula below).

*Cooling Energy Use = Total Use – Non-Cooling Electric Use*

*Cooling Energy Use = 858,560 – 638,800 = 219,760 kWh/year*

4. Enter this total on the allocation form, as shown on Line E-9, Column D of Figure A-4.

Note that the dotted line in Figure A-5 nearly intersects the lowest points on the total kWh per day graph. This is appropriate for our example building, which is in

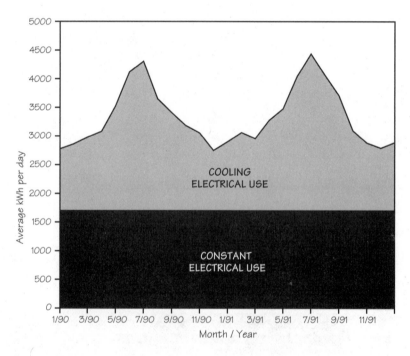

Figure A-6. Graph illustrating the pattern of annual electric use for buildings in warm climates with chilling as the only weather-variable energy consumer. Unlike a cold climate, there is air conditioning energy use all year.

a climate where there is almost no cooling required during the winter months. In a climate where cooling is required all year, the graph would look like Figure A-6, which depicts a building where the winter cooling load is approximately 20% of the summer cooling load.

Using this graphic method of depicting the division between weather-variable and constant electrical users allows the energy manager to judge the accuracy of the allocation. If, for example, the constant electrical use line in Figure A-5 fell at the 2,000 kWh per day level, it would be clear that the constant electrical users had been overestimated. If the dotted line was drawn at the 1,000 kWh per day level, it would indicate that a significant amount of constant use was not yet accounted for.

## Buildings with Electrical Chillers and Electrical Heating Boilers

In cases where there is both a cooling and heating component, the weather-variable electrical use can be divided between heating and cooling by using a graphical method consisting of these steps:

1. Make a graph of the monthly electric consumption, as shown in Figure 4-5 (page 56) and A-5.

2. Estimate the constant electrical energy consumers, as previously described.

3. Draw a horizontal line on the graph to represent the constant electrical energy consumption.

4. Extend the heating and cooling use curves to approximate their use pattern (see Figure A-7).

5. Looking at the graph, estimate the amount of total monthly energy allocated for heating, cooling and constant uses, and enter that number on a spreadsheet similar to the one shown in Figure A-8.

6. Total the annual use for heating and cooling and enter the results in the allocation summary.

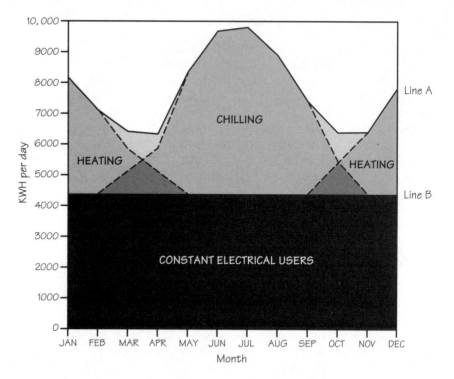

Figure A-7. Graph illustrating the pattern of annual electric use for buildings with electrical chillers and electrical heating boilers.

Figure A-8. Annual electric use in tabular form, based on Figure A-7.

| A Month | B Daily Average (kWh/day) | C Non-weather Variable (kWh/day) | D Heating & Chilling Combined | E Assigned to Heating | F Assigned to Cooling |
|---|---|---|---|---|---|
| JAN | 8,100 | 4,383 | 3,817 | 3,817 | 0 |
| FEB | 7,100 | 4,383 | 2,717 | 2,717 | 0 |
| MAR | 6,400 | 4,383 | 2,017 | 1,500 | 517 |
| APR | 6,300 | 4,383 | 1,917 | 1,000 | 917 |
| MAY | 8,300 | 4,383 | 3,917 | 0 | 3,917 |
| JUN | 9,700 | 4,383 | 5,317 | 0 | 5,317 |
| JUL | 9,800 | 4,383 | 5,417 | 0 | 5,417 |
| AUG | 8,900 | 4,383 | 4,417 | 0 | 4,417 |
| SEP | 7,400 | 4,383 | 3,017 | 0 | 3,017 |
| OCT | 6,400 | 4,383 | 2,017 | 1,000 | 1,017 |
| NOV | 6,400 | 4,383 | 2.017 | 2,017 | 0 |
| DEC | 7,800 | 4,383 | 3,417 | 3,417 | 0 |
| TOTALS | | | 40,004 | 15,468 | 24,536 |

### Example of the Graphical Method for Allocating Electric Consumption for Heating and Cooling

To illustrate this method, a 100,000-square-foot office building is chosen as an example (this is not the example used throughout the book). The building has a total annual electrical consumption of 2,800,000 kilowatt hours. Estimates of the annual use by constant consumers total 1,600,000 kilowatt hours. The remaining 1,200,000 kilowatt hours are consumed by the chillers and boilers. Following the graphical method:

1. The graph of one year's average daily electrical use is shown in Figure A-7; Line A represents the annual use profile.

2. Divide 1,600,000 kWh/hr by 365 days to determine the average daily use of all constant items: 4,383 kWh per day.

3. Draw a horizontal line (Line B on Figure A-7) on the graph to represent the average daily use for constant consumption. The shaded area above Line B now represents the combined chilling and heating electrical use.

4. Add the dotted lines to approximate the individual shapes of the chilling curve and the heating curve.

5. Enter the average daily electrical consumption for each month in Column B of the spreadsheet (Figure A-8). Subtract 4,383 kWh (the daily average use for constant consumption in Column C) from each month's total average use and enter that value in Column D. This is the total energy for chilling and heating combined. Then, looking at the graph, divide the total in Column D between heating and chilling and enter in Columns E and F.

6. Total Columns D, E and F of Figure A-8. These totals represent the annual sum of the average daily use in each month. Multiply these numbers by 30 days per month to approximate the annual use in each category as follows:

   Annual Heating Estimate = 15,468 kWh x 30 = 464,040 kWh/yr
   Annual Cooling Estimate = 24,536 kWh x 30 = 736,080 kWh/yr

## Buildings That Use Heat Pumps, Electric Boilers, and Cooling Towers

The process of estimating the weather-variable electrical use in buildings equipped with heat pumps is nearly identical to the method used in the previous example. The first step is to total the estimates of constant electrical use and subtract this total from the billed annual electrical consumption (Line C in Figure A-9). The remainder then must be divided between three components: the heat pumps, the tower that cools the core water loop in summer, and the boiler that adds heat to the core water loop in the winter.

The graph of monthly electrical use for a 100,000-square-foot office building equipped with heat pumps would look like Line A in Figure A-9 (this is not the example used throughout the book). The winter and summer peaks are not pronounced because they are formed by the boiler and the cooling tower, which are a relatively small portion of the weather-variable total. The bulk of this total is usually composed of the heat pump compressors and fans, which operate more or less constantly throughout the year.

The area above Line C, represents the weather-variable electrical use.  It can be divided into three components by first drawing a horizontal line (Line B) slightly below the lowest point of Line A to represent the separation between heat pump fans and compressors (the area between Lines B and C), and the energy used by the boiler and cooling towers (the area between Lines A and B).  The cooling tower energy use can then be separated from the boiler electrical use by adding the sloping lines shown in Figure A-9.  In this example, the sloping dotted lines are based on the assumption that the cooling tower begins operating in March and ends in October, and the boiler begins heating in September and ends in April.  The boiler and cooling tower electrical use can then be quantified using the method described in a previous example, illustrated in Figures A-7 and A-8.

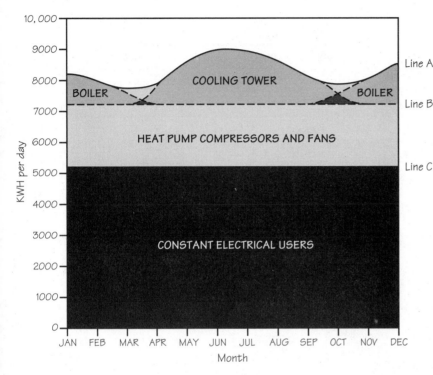

Figure A-9. Graph illustrating the pattern of annual electric use for buildings with heat pumps, electric boilers, and cooling towers.

## COMPLETING THE ELECTRICAL ALLOCATION

The goal of the electrical estimating process is to produce an allocation form similar to Figure A-10, with Columns C and D filled in. When the allocation form has achieved this level of completion the energy manager should return to Task 4 of Chapter 4 (page 61) for instructions in completing the electrical allocation.

**ELECTRICAL ENERGY USE**

Item A: $0.053 per kWh

| B | C | D | E | F |
|---|---|---|---|---|
| | Item | Estimated annual kWh | Annual cost | Percent of total cost |
| Constant electrical uses | E-1. Lighting | 194,700 | | |
| | E-2. Air handling fans | 225,390 | | |
| | E-3. Office equipment | 102,345 | | |
| | E-4. Exhaust fans | 9,610 | | |
| | E-5. Elevators | 20,900 | | |
| | E-6. | | | |
| | E-7. Miscellaneous | 85,856 | | |
| | E-8. Subtotals | 638,800 | $33,856 | |
| Weather-variable electrical uses | E-9. Air conditioning | 219,760 | | |
| | E-10. | | | |
| | E-11. Subtotals | 219,760 | | |
| | E-12. Electric totals | 858,560 | $45,081 | |

Figure A-10. Electrical energy use is allocated to the individual devices and systems.

# APPENDIX B

# Estimating the Annual Cost to Operate Fuel-Consuming Devices

This appendix describes simplified methods to estimate the annual energy dollars consumed by devices that use fuel. The examples are designed for buildings whose fuel source is natural gas, because it is used by the vast majority of the facilities for which this book is written. However, the methods can easily be adapted for facilities that consume fuel oil, propane, district steam or coal.

The estimating process begins with the creation of a form on which the results of all the individual estimates can be summarized. The form shown in Figure B-1 is recommended and is used in the examples throughout this book. The first step is to enter in Column C the significant fuel users that were listed in Chapter 3 (Figure 3-7 on page 34). Note that the items have been subdivided into constant and weather-variable fuel consumers. Next, the total known annual fuel consumption determined in Chapter 5 (see Figure 5-3 on page 66) is entered on the form at the bottom of Column D. This known total will be allocated to the various fuel users.

It is important to pay close attention to the units used to express gas consumption and billed gas amounts. Gas bills typically express quantities in ccf (hundreds of cubic feet) or in mcf (thousands of cubic feet). For the purposes of these estimates, it will be assumed that 1 cubic foot of gas contains 1,000 Btu. Therefore, a ccf equals 100,000 Btu and an mcf represents 1,000,000 Btu.

**FUEL ENERGY USE**

| Item A: $0.452 per ccf (fuel cost) |
|---|

Figure B-1. Allocation of annual fuel energy cost— items are listed and total fuel use and cost are known.

| B | C | D | E | F |
|---|---|---|---|---|
| | Item | Estimated annual ccf | Annual cost | Percent of total cost |
| Constant natural gas uses | F-1. Domestic hot water | | | |
| | F-2. | | | |
| | F-3. Subtotals: | | | |
| Weather-variable natural gas uses | F-4. Space heating | | | |
| | F-5. | | | |
| | F-6. Subtotals: | | | |
| | F-7. Natural gas totals | 35,483 | $16,038 | |

## ESTIMATING CONSTANT FUEL CONSUMERS

Heating domestic hot water is a typical use of fuel energy in buildings. Unlike space heating, this type of heating does not vary with the weather, and consumption can be considered constant for estimating purposes.

The annual consumption of natural gas for hot water heating can be quickly estimated by determining the amount of hot water used daily by the occupants and multiplying by the gas consumption per gallon. This estimate is based on the assumption that gas water heaters consume approximately 730 Btu for each gallon of water heated. To estimate energy use for gas water heating, follow these steps:

1. Estimate the average gallons of hot water used by each occupant each day.

2. Multiply this average consumption by the total number of occupants to obtain total daily gallons heated.

3. Multiply the total daily use by 730 Btu per gallon to obtain total daily Btu used.

4. Multiply total daily usage by the number of work days during the year to get Btu per year.

5. Divide Btu per year by 100,000 to get ccf per year.

## Summary of Constant Fuel Consumers

Although only domestic hot water consumption is considered here, natural gas or other fuels may also be used to supply other constant energy needs that do not vary with the weather (i.e., cooking, drying, etc.). These fuel uses can be roughly estimated by obtaining the burner input rating from the nameplate and multiplying it by an estimate of the hours per year of operation. Once the estimates for the fuel energy uses presented in this task are completed, they should be entered into the fuels allocation form, as shown in Figure B-2.

---

### Example of Calculation Method for Gas Water Heating

Our example office building is occupied by 300 workers, and it is estimated that each person uses 2 gallons of lavatory hot water each day. The annual gas use for water heating can be approximated as follows:

320 workers x 2 gal/day x 730 Btu/gal = 467,200 Btu per day

467,200 Btu per day x 260 work days/yr = 121,472,000 Btu/yr

$$\frac{121,472,000 \text{ Btu/yr}}{100,000 \text{ Btu/ccf}} = 1,214 \text{ ccf per year}$$

Enter on Line F-1 of Column D of Figure B-2.

---

**FUEL ENERGY USE**

Item A: $0.452 per ccf (fuel cost)

Figure B-2. Allocation of annual fuel energy cost— constant fuel uses are filled in first.

| B | C | D | E | F |
|---|---|---|---|---|
| FUEL USE (Natural gas) | Item | Estimated annual ccf | Annual cost | Percent of total cost |
| Constant natural gas uses | F-1. Domestic hot water | 1,214 | | |
| | F-2. | | | |
| | F-3. Subtotals: | 1,214 | | |
| Weather-variable natural gas uses | F-4. Space heating | | | |
| | F-5. | | | |
| | F-6. Subtotals: | | | |
| | F-7. Natural gas totals | 35,483 | $16,038 | |

## ESTIMATING WEATHER-DEPENDENT FUEL CONSUMERS

Calculating the precise annual natural gas use of heating and cooling systems (which vary with the weather) can be a very complex procedure requiring considerable knowledge of heating load and cooling load calculating procedures. The purpose of these energy use estimates is to gain a general knowledge of the relative proportion of the annual total that can be assigned to each major energy-consuming system.

The simplest approach to estimating heating and cooling energy use is to first estimate the annual use of all of the non-weather variable users and then subtract this number from the total annual fuel energy use derived from the utility bills. This approach is illustrated below for the example building.

### Estimating Gas-Fired Boiler Energy Use

In many buildings, space heating boilers are the only weather-related equipment using fuels. The example building used throughout the book fits this description: it is a 67,000-square-foot office building located in a northern United States climate, with two gas-fired boilers as the only weather-variable gas consumers. The only other natural gas consumption—for providing domestic hot water—is not weather related.

Two parallel approaches can be used to estimate annual gas consumption for the boilers—a calculation method and a graphical method.

## Calculation Method

If the estimates of the constant uses are relatively complete and reliable, a simple calculation procedure is sufficient to determine annual gas-fired boiler use.

1. Find the total annual natural gas use on Line F-7, Column D of the fuel allocation form.

2. Find the total annual constant fuel use on Line F-3, Column D of the fuel allocation form.

3. Subtract the constant fuel use from the total fuel use to obtain the heating use (see formula below):

Heating Energy Use = Total Use − Constant Fuel Use
Heating Energy Use = 35,483 ccf − 1,214 ccf = 34,269 ccf

4. Enter this total on Lines F-4 and F-6, Column D of the allocation summary form as shown in Figure B-3.

**FUEL ENERGY USE**

Item A: $0.452 per ccf (fuel cost)

| B | C | D | E | F |
|---|---|---|---|---|
| FUEL USE (Natural gas) | Item | Estimated annual ccf | Annual cost | Percent of total cost |
| Constant natural gas uses | F-1. Domestic hot water | 1,214 | | |
| | F-2. | | | |
| | F-3. Subtotals: | 1,214 | | |
| Weather-variable natural gas uses | F-4. Space heating | 34,269 | | |
| | F-5. | | | |
| | F-6. Subtotals: | 34,269 | | |
| | F-7. Natural gas totals | 35,483 | $16,038 | |

Figure B-3. Allocation of annual fuel energy cost—weather-related fuel uses are filled in after completing constant uses.

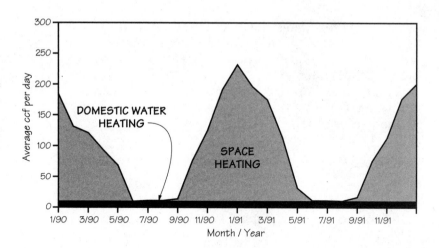

Figure B-4. Graph illustrating the pattern of annual fuel use for buildings with gas-fired boilers.

## Graphical Method

It is also possible to make a rough estimate of natural gas used for heating by using a graphical method. The graph of the fuel use from Task 1 in Chapter 5 is shown here as Figure B-4. A line is drawn on the plot, connecting the summer month valleys. This represents a separation between the annual heating fuel use (area above the line) and the constant fuel use (area below the line).

Using this graph, the total annual consumption for the two categories of fuel use can be calculated by following these steps:

1. Calculate the area below the dashed line (domestic hot water fuel use) as follows:

   Average daily use × 365 days = Constant annual use

   Approximately 7 ccf × 365 days = 2,555 ccf per year

2. Calculate the remaining area above the dashed line (space heating) as follows:

   Total annual use − Constant annual use = Space heating use

   35,483 ccf (1991) − 2,555 ccf = 32,928 ccf per year

3. This total could be placed on Lines F-4 and F-6 of the allocation form.

Both of these methods should provide a reasonable approximation of the heating energy use as a portion of the total annual fuel consumption.

## Buildings That Use Gas for Cooling

For buildings in warm climates that are cooled by gas-fired absorptive refrigeration, cooling gas use can be estimated by using methods similar to those described in the example above.

The natural gas use profile for a gas-cooled building would look similar to Line A in Figure B-5. The average daily gas use of domestic water heating can be estimated using the methods described previously and graphically depicted by Line B in Figure B-5. In this case, the shaded area above Line B represents an approximation of the gas used for cooling.

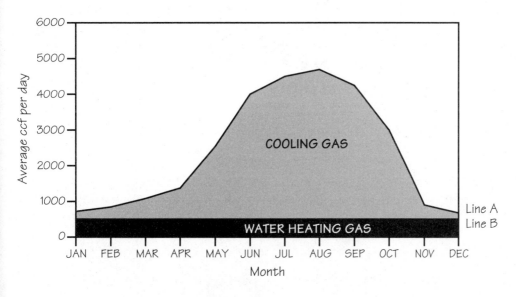

Figure B-5. Graph illustrating the pattern of annual fuel use for buildings with gas used for cooling.

## Buildings That Use Gas for Heating and Cooling

In cases where there is more than one weather-variable component, the total fuel use for all weather-variable equipment can be divided among its major contributors (e.g., chillers, boilers) by using a graphical method that consists of these steps:

1. Make a spreadsheet and graph of the monthly fuel consumption.

2. Estimate the constant fuel energy consumers.

3. Draw a horizontal line on the graph to represent the constant fuel consumption.

4. Extend the heating and cooling use curves to approximate their use pattern.

5. Looking at the graph; estimate the amount of total monthly energy allocated for heating, cooling and non-weather-related uses; and enter this number on a new spreadsheet.

6. Total the annual use for each major weather-variable fuel-consuming system and enter the results in the allocation summary for the building.

The following example on the next page illustrates the use of this method.

## Example of the Graphical Method for Allocating Fuel Consumption for Heating and Cooling

To illustrate this method, an office building is chosen as an example (this is not the example used throughout the book). The building has a total annual fuel consumption of 42,720 ccf. An estimate of the annual use by the only constant consumer, water heating, totals 2,520 ccf. The remaining 40,200 ccf is consumed by the chillers and boilers. The following illustrates the use of the graphical method:

1. The graph of one year's average daily fuel use is shown in Figure B-6, with Line A representing the annual use profile.

2. Divide 2,520 ccf by 365 days to determine the average daily use of all constant items (domestic hot water): 7 ccf per day.

3. Draw a horizontal line (Line B on Figure B-6) on the graph to represent the average daily use for constant fuel users. The shaded area above Line B now represents the combined chilling and heating fuel use.

4. Add the dotted lines to approximate the individual shapes of the chilling curve and the heating curve in the spring and fall months when both heating and chilling take place.

5. Enter the average daily fuel consumption for each month in Column B of the spreadsheet (Figure B-7). Subtract 7 ccf (the daily average use for domestic hot water consumption in Column C) from each month's total average use, and enter that value in Column D. This is the total energy for chilling and heating combined. Then, looking at the graph, divide the total in Column D into heating and chilling, and enter these numbers into Columns E and F.

6. Total Columns D, E and F of Figure B-7. These totals represent the annual sum of the average daily use in each month. Multiply the totals in Columns E and F by 30 days per month to approximate the annual use in each category as follows:

   Annual Heating Estimate = 492 ccf x 30 days = 14,760 ccf/yr
   Annual Cooling Estimate = 848 ccf x 30 days = 25,440 ccf/yr

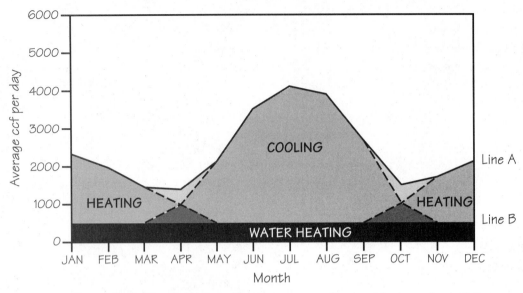

Figure B-6. Graph illustrating the pattern of annual fuel use for buildings with gas used for heating and cooling.

Figure B-7. Annual fuel use in tabular form based on Figure B-6.

| A | B | C | D | E | F |
|---|---|---|---|---|---|
| Month | Monthly Average (CCF/day) | Domestic Hot Water (CCF/day) | Heating & Cooling Combined | Assigned to Heating | Assigned to Cooling |
| JAN | 117 | 7 | 110 | 110 | 0 |
| FEB | 100 | 7 | 93 | 93 | 0 |
| MAR | 76 | 7 | 69 | 69 | 0 |
| APR | 73 | 7 | 66 | 30 | 36 |
| MAY | 102 | 7 | 95 | 0 | 95 |
| JUN | 175 | 7 | 168 | 0 | 168 |
| JUL | 202 | 7 | 195 | 0 | 195 |
| AUG | 198 | 7 | 191 | 0 | 191 |
| SEP | 130 | 7 | 123 | 0 | 123 |
| OCT | 72 | 7 | 65 | 25 | 40 |
| NOV | 77 | 7 | 70 | 70 | 0 |
| DEC | 102 | 7 | 95 | 95 | 0 |
| TOTALS | 1,424 | 84 | 1,340 | 492 | 848 |

**FUEL ENERGY USE**

Item A: $0.452 per ccf (fuel cost)

| B | C | D | E | F |
|---|---|---|---|---|
| FUEL USE (Natural gas) | Item | Estimated annual ccf | Annual cost | Percent of total cost |
| Constant natural gas uses | F-1. Domestic hot water | 1,214 | | |
| | F-2. | | | |
| | F-3. Subtotals: | 1,214 | | |
| Weather-variable natural gas uses | F-4. Space heating | 34,269 | | |
| | F-5. | | | |
| | F-6. Subtotals: | 34,269 | | |
| | F-7. Natural gas totals | 35,483 | $16,038 | |

Figure B-8. Fuel energy use is allocated to the individual devices and systems.

## COMPLETING THE FUELS ALLOCATION

The goal of estimating the fuel use is to produce an allocation form similar to Figure B-8, with Columns C and D filled in. When the allocation form is filled in to this level, the energy manager should return to Task 4 of Chapter 5 (page 73) for instructions to complete the fuels allocation.

# APPENDIX C

# Estimating Demand Costs

This appendix describes a method to allocate electrical demand (kW) cost separately from kilowatt hour (kWh) costs. This is useful to the more advanced energy manager in facilities where demand charges represent a significant portion of the total electrical cost (35 percent or more). By estimating the kW cost and the kWh cost separately for each item, the energy manager can more accurately predict the savings that will result from improved operation. This concept is illustrated by the following example:

———

An energy manager determined that the lights in a storeroom ran continuously and cost $600 per year to operate—$400 per year for kWh and $200 per year for demand charges. In evaluating the potential to save some portion of this cost, it was noted that if the storeroom lights could be turned off 25 percent of the time, the savings would be 25 percent of the $400 kWh cost, or $100. However, none of the $200 kW cost would be saved unless the lights were off during the period of monthly peak demand. If, for example, they could be turned off during the peak period six months per year, one-half of the $200 kW cost, or $100, would be saved. Knowing that the storeroom was used intermittently throughout the day, the energy manager decided that it was unrealistic to expect the lights to be off during peak demand periods, and instead focused his attention on saving some portion of the $400 per year kWh costs only.

———

This example illustrates how the knowledge of kWh and kW costs for each item permits a more realistic evaluation of the savings potential and usually results in a more sophisticated plan to manage the efficient operation of the device under study.

## ALLOCATING DEMAND COSTS

Chapter 4 describes methods for organizing electrical bill information into a spreadsheet that tabulates monthly billed kWh and assigns a cost each month that represents a blend of the kW and the kWh costs. In Figure 4-3, an example spreadsheet shows monthly kWh in Column B and the total cost in Column E. The primary concept for allocating kW and kWh costs separately is to create two separate spreadsheets, similar to Figure 4-3: one for kWh and one for kW.

The first step is to create a spreadsheet similar to Figure 4-3, following the instructions in Chapter 4, but entering in Column E only the kWh cost as indicated on utility bills. This is the only alteration to the procedures described in Chapter 4.

The next step is to create an electrical demand, kW spreadsheet similar to Figure C-1. Column B contains the kW shown on the monthly bills, and Column C contains the kW costs typically itemized separately on electric bills. Column D contains the unit cost. Notice that in the example building, the kW costs are $8.30 per kW per month in the four summer months and $5.60 per kW per month in the other eight months of the year.

The third step is to create a graph of the data in Column B in order to produce a graph of the billed monthly kW for an entire year (see Figure C-2).

The final step is to create a kW allocation form as shown in Figure C-3. The following paragraphs describe the origins of the information in this allocation form.

The unit costs for demand are entered at Item A. Note that in this example building, the summer demand charges differ from the winter demand charges. Note also that a "blended" demand charge has been calculat-

Figure C-1. 1991 electrical demand for example office building.

| A<br>Month | B<br>Total kW | C<br>kW Cost | D<br>Unit Cost |
|---|---|---|---|
| JAN | 152 | $851 | $5.60 |
| FEB | 160 | $896 | $5.60 |
| MAR | 174 | $974 | $5.60 |
| APR | 182 | $1,019 | $5.60 |
| MAY | 230 | $1,288 | $5.60 |
| JUN | 236 | $1,958 | $8.30 |
| JUL | 262 | $2,174 | $8.30 |
| AUG | 255 | $2,116 | $8.30 |
| SEP | 240 | $1,992 | $8.30 |
| OCT | 212 | $1,187 | $5.60 |
| NOV | 171 | $957 | $5.60 |
| DEC | 160 | $896 | $5.60 |
| TOTALS | 2,434 | $16,308 | |

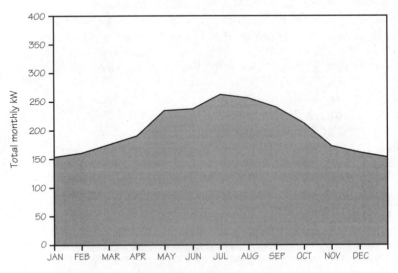

Figure C-2. Graph of monthly kW.

ed, representing the average for the entire year. The formula for this calculation is:

average kW charge = $\dfrac{(\$8.30 \times 4\ months) + (\$5.60 \times 8\ months)}{12\ months}$

average kW charge = $6.50

    Columns B and C are identical to the same Columns used in Appendix A (Figure A-1) to allocate the kWh costs.

    Column D contains the estimates of each item's contribution to the total annual kW. Note that the total kW taken from the bills and entered at the bottom of Column B in Figure C-1 is entered at the bottom of Column D on Line E-12. This is the total annual kW that needs to be allocated to all of the electricity-consuming devices.

    Methods for estimating the annual kW for each of the items can be found in Appendix A. Note that the formulas there typically calculate a kW amount for each item (prior to multiplying it by the hours per year to derive kWh per year). The kW number in those formulas must then be multiplied by the number of months per year that item is expected to contribute to peak. The following example illustrates this method.

    An example of the *lighting take-off method* is given on page 153. In this example, the total lighting kW—i.e., the contribution lighting makes to peak demand—was calculated to be 44.8 kilowatts. It can be assumed that this lighting operates all year and therefore will make the same contribution to demand each month. The annual kW then would be:

    44.8 kW x 12 months = 537.6 kW

    This number would be entered on the demand allocation form on Line E-1, Column D.

    Using the estimating methods in Appendix A to determine kW and multiplying by the appropriate number of months will provide estimates of the kW that can be entered for each item in Column D.

The method for estimating air-conditioning demand is similar to the methods for estimating air-conditioning kWh described in Appendix A. In this case, the graph of monthly total kW (Figure C-2) can be used to estimate the added cooling season kW that results from air conditioning. In Figure C-2, a horizontal line can be drawn at approximately 175 kW, and it can be assumed that all kW above that line result from the air conditioning. By subtracting 175 from the total kW in months May through October and summing these remainders, an approximation of air conditioning kW can be made. That number can then be entered on Line E-9 of Column D.

Note that the total kW assigned to the items in Column C should equal the total billed kW entered on Line E-12 of Column D.

The unit cost that is appropriate to the items can be entered in Column E. Any items that contribute to peak load year-round can use the average cost ($6.50 in the example); any items that are known to operate only in the winter (e.g., electric snow-melting) would use a unit cost of $5.60, and any items known to operate only during summer months (air conditioning, in this example) would use the $8.30 figure.

Column F represents the product of multiplying Column D by Column E. This is the annual kW cost assigned to each item.

Column G uses the same graph used in Appendix A. It is simply a graph of the annual kW costs shown in Column F.

## COMBINING ALLOCATIONS

The final step in this allocation process is to combine the kW allocation with the kWh allocation and the fuel allocation, to complete the total cost allocation for the facility. This is done by simply combining Figure C-3 with the other two allocations shown in Figure 6-2. This figure would then have three components, rather than two, completing the total energy cost allocation process.

## Figure C-3. Allocation of electrical demand cost.

**Item A. Unit Costs**
Summer: $8.30 per kW (4 months per year)
Winter: $5.60 per kW (8 months per year)
Average: $6.50 per kW (12 month average)

| B | C | D | E | F | G |
|---|---|---|---|---|---|
| | Item | Estimated annual kW | Unit cost per kW | Annual kW cost | Graph of cost per year (thousands of dollars) 0  4  8  12  16 |
| Constant electrical uses | E-1. Lighting | 538 | $6.50 | $3500 | |
| | E-2. Air handling fans | 440 | $6.50 | $2860 | |
| | E-3. Office equipment | 680 | $6.50 | $4420 | |
| | E-4. Exhaust fans | 80 | $6.50 | $520 | |
| | E-5. Elevators | 160 | $6.50 | $1040 | |
| | E-6. | | | | |
| | E-7. Miscellaneous | 151 | $6.50 | $980 | |
| | E-8. Subtotals | | | | |
| Weather-variable electrical uses | E-9. Air conditioning | 385 | $8.30 | $3195 | |
| | E-10. | | | | |
| | E-11. Subtotals | | | | |
| | E-12. Electric totals | 2434 | | 16,515 | |

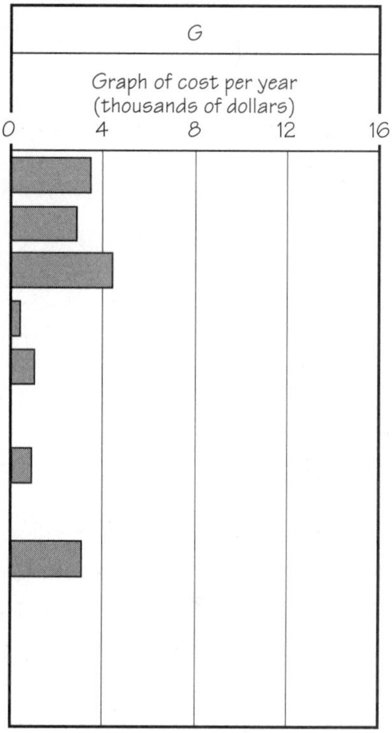